BOATBUILDER'S MANUAL

BOATBUILDER'S MANUAL

Edited and Illustrated by
Charles C. Walbridge

with
Steve Rock on *Vacuum Bagging and Epoxy Resins*
Gary E. Myers on *Health and Safety*
Chip Queitzsch on *Laminate Design*

MENASHA RIDGE PRESS,

Sixth edition, fourth printing
Printed in the United States of America

Library of Congress Cataloging-in-Publication Data
Boatbuilder's manual.
I. Canoes and canoeing–Design and construction. 2. Kayaks–Design and construction. 3. Fiberglass boats–Design and construction. I. Walbridge, Charles C., 1948-
VM353.B64 1986 623.8'29 86-12739
ISBN 0-89732-022-0

Cover photo of New Wave Kayaks by John Schreiner
Cover design by Mary Mendell

Menasha Ridge Press
3169 Cahaba Heights Road
Birmingham, AL 35243

CONTENTS

INTRODUCTION:

When I began paddling white water boats in the late 60's, every boater was a builder. Except for imports and a few basement operations, there was no other way to get a kayak or C-1. It was some years later, after a ferocious boatbuilding binge in an old garage in Lewisburg, Pa., I sat down to write a few brief notes on construction and materials. Fifteen years, six revisions, and 24,000 copies later, this project is clearly getting out of hand! I have tried to grow with the sport. River runners and racers are pushing back the old limits, demanding more and more from their boats in the process. Manufacturers have matured into well-established business, and the market is now dominated by materials other than fiberglass. But one thing remains constant despite all the changes and improvements: your best value in boats is the one you build yourself.

Building a kayak or canoe is not easy. It is no accident that the vastly increased availability of commercially-built craft has cut deeply into the ranks of the homebuilder. Although the job is not highly skilled, it is complex and cannot be rushed. The materials are at best obnoxious; at worst highly toxic, and all demand careful handling if you are to successsfully complete the project. The key to success is craftsmanship, and craftsmanship is founded on patience. Attempts to rush the process lead to mistakes, which leads to frustration and even more problems. To succeed. you must look upon the job ahead as an experience to be enjoyed rather than as a task to be rushed through. While there are few problems which cannot be fixed with a bit of TLC, anyone who tries to find shortcuts is going to end up with frayed nerves and a full trash can. Leave the speed contest to the factory boys with their production quotas and deadlines! In time you'll be ready to savor the satisfaction of paddling a boat you made yourself; the pleasure of owning a truly custom-made river machine, and save over 50% of the price of a comparable commercial product to the bargain.

Since the last edition, we have made efforts to have the book checked by knowledgeable people. In this regard, I must thank Chip Queitzch and John Sweet for their helpful and thorough commentary in what has been an unending effort by engineers to enlighten an unrepentant liberal arts major. This book has benefitted for years from the help of others like them: Norman Holcombe, the late Martin Begun, Bruce Weber, George Hendricks, Frank Birdsong, Dave and Dan Demaree, Bill McKnight, John Brown, Bill Clark, Payson Kennedy, Jack Wright, and a host of other fellow-experimenters. Gary Myers, Jim Colianne, and Steve Rock contributed by writing sections on parts of the boatbuilding world outside my experience. But these folks and others like them could not have done what they did were it not for the true pioneers: Dave Kurtz, John Berry, Jim Raleigh, Bart Hauthaway, Stuart Coffin, and Ted Waddell. Working from boats brought over from Europe, these men began investigating the possibilities of reinforced plastics and made tentative attempts at boat design. For this edition I had the pleasure of "picking the brains" of Jesse Whittemore and John Schriner, two excellent semi-commercial builders with lots of practical advice.

So lets get to it! Your comments are, as always, of interest to me, and you are invited to send them to 230 Penllyn Pike, Penllyn, PA 19422. Remember: when better canoes and kayaks are built, paddlers will build them.

See you on the river,

Charlie

Charlie Walbridge, Editor

"WOOPS...."

NOTES ON THE BOATS:

Whitewater boats, like most things used by many different people, come in a bewildering array of shapes and sizes. While there are hundreds of different designs, each with its own purpose, there are really only two types: kayaks and canoes. Kayaks are fully-decked, self-contained craft paddled from a sitting position with a double-bladed paddle. Canoes are wider and tippier, and are usually paddled from a kneeling position with a single-bladed paddle. You can further make the distinction between standard "open" canoes and fully decked C-1's; the former are beamier, bulkier, and better suited to easier rapids. Tandem canoes, or C-2's, are quite popular and are frequently molded; two-seater kayaks, on the other hand, while popular in Europe, are seldom seen on this side of the Atlantic. Each boat has its own personality, and a unique combination of strengths and weaknesses. Let's look at each one:

Kayaks are by far the most popular boat for serious river-running. Its double-bladed paddle gives the user the efficiency of a symmetrical stroke and the security of having a brace on both sides. There are fewer stokes to learn, and maneuvering is relatively simple. Most people can pick up the basics on flat-water in a few hours, and someone who has little spare time for practice will get the most out of this type of boat for his effort. On long cruises, the sitting position is said to be more comfortable and less tiring. But there are drawbacks. You sit lower in the water, which is colder, and reduces visibility in complex rapids. Big men (those over 175 pounds) often find the seating arrangements cramped, and the boat tippier than they would like. They also find that their weight, combined with the boat's small size, causes them to plunge through large waves, miss eddies, and to drop deeper into holes and hydraulics. Furthermore, there have been a number of serious accidents in which the deck of a kayak collapsed on the occupant's legs, pinning him in place. The consensus among experts is that K-1's are excellent for big-water paddling, but must be used with some caution on tight, technical streams. The single kayak class is viciously competitive at most races, with top athletes separated by a few seconds. You'll have to train long and hard to even begin to do well.

C-1's are well-distributed throughout the East, but are little known on the other side of the Missisippi. Many people find them too uncomfortable to paddle seriously, and even the die-hards admit that the kneeling position takes some getting used to. A single-bladed paddle, furthermore, is not efficient. The boat does not like to go in a straight line, and considerable energy is expended in steering. Stroke combinations are complex and require much practice, but the biggest difficulty lies in developing the drive needed to break through holes and surf waves. All of this is very frustrating to the learner, particularly when there are kayaks around, so most "C-boaters" are converted open canoeists, or come from an area where these boats are common and coaching is plentiful. But after a while its advantages begin to show. It's a bigger boat, with higher volume, and well suited to carrying a big man. Although lacking a brace on one side, the leverage which can be developed on the other is pretty incredible, and will keep the boat upright in situations when kayaks will be rolling. The kneeling position allows a better view of the onrushing water, and the higher center of gravity permits faster, tighter turns. And because a canoeist does not sit under the deck, there's less danger of being pinned inside a collapsing boat. And unless you live in the Middle Atlantic States, where 90% of the nation's C-boaters reside, you can with a little conditioning and practice do well at local races. Out West, there are some places where you'll be considered a novelty, not a class, but they're learning !

C-2's are exceptionally demanding to paddle because they require teamwork in addition to skill. While a good pair can run even the most technical drops with the speed of a kayak and the security of a C-1, let it be said from the start that it takes more than two first-rate paddlers to form a team! The technical aspects are far less complex than the human side; timing and trust can only be developed through hours of practice. Because many pairs have difficulty developing a reliable river roll, mistakes are frustrating and often costly. This boat has wrecked marriages and ruined long-term friendships, particularly on the racing circuit. Unless you are able to forget your ego for a while (which is easier said than done) and concentrate on coordinating with your partner to make the boat perform, you'd better get back into a single-seat craft. And while a C-2 is a great way to show someone the joys of cruising an easy river in relative safety, it is not recommended for beginners, as most forget technique and yell at each other. Better develop some skill, so you can see what errors are due to technique and which come from lack of teamwork. Most white water designs put both cockpits near the ends for greater leverage, but "center-cockpit" designs, originally made for racing, have much promise for cruising types as well. A few of the old designs have a center cockpit, which converts a C-2 into a rather clumsy, sluggish C-1 and gives access to the center for the storage of duffel.

Two seater kayaks are uncommon in America, and are seldom used in rapids. They are hard to turn and difficult to roll, so few successful teams have developed. Their easy speed has made them quite popular in Europe for mild-water touring over long distances. Most of the K-2's and K-4's in this country are made for Olympic-style flatwater racing. Because of the advantages of having a completely rigid hull, and the fact that Olympic rules specify a certain minimum weight, fiberglass "shells," be they canoes or kayaks, are considered inferior to those made of wood. As competitors become more familiar with the new materials described in this book, this is bound to change, but the tippy Olympic designs require much practice to use, and are unlikely to become common in this country.

Open canoes have been used in whitewater throughout North America for generations, and are extremely popular in the East, Midwest, and Canada. Many lengths and designs are avaliable from 12-18 feet long, from the unsophisticated "universal hull shape" to designs made precisely for touring, slalom racing, marathon-style paddling, or whatever. The "Allaround" hull is an extremely versitile shape, and is at home on lakes rivers, swamps, and ocean. It can take you on a lengthy wilderness trip, carry the wife and kids on a summer jaunt, serve as a duck blind or fishing float and, in the right hands, run Class V whitewater. But its homely appearance makes it the target of epithets slung by the hardcore enthusiasts; the whitewater folk say it's "unresponsive" and "piggy", while the flatwater set vows to forsake these "bruisewaters" for boats with a thinner, sleeker hull shape. Such specialized boats are less versitile, but because they are produced in smaller numbers, more likely to be made in fiberglass than the "All-American" hull. The selection guidelines on hull shape for decked boats applies equally to standard canoes; and while there are reasons for the short 13' "solo boats" and the 20'+ "war canoes", most people prefer lenths of between 16 and 18 feet. And although somewhat limited compared to the whitewater capabilities of a decked craft, the additional challenge is one which a certain type of person finds intriguing.

WIDTH: The wider a boat, the more inherently stable it will be. Narrow boats are tippier, but faster paddling, since less of the hull is in contact with the water. Minimum widths for decked boats has been set by the ICF, and almost all standard designs adhere closely to it. the wider "touring boats", while more stable for the novice, are very difficult to roll or brace. They are not recommended except to those soley interested in casual touring. Some race boats, while meeting minimum requirements, are substantially narrower at the waterline than the usual craft. These finicky designs are for experts only, unless, of course, you enjoy getting wet. Open canoes vary greatly in width, according to their size and your needs. Be aware of anything which strays from the norm unless you are a specialist.

VOLUME: The bigger a boat, the greater its buoyancy, and the higher it will float in turbulent water. "High Volume" boats are more stable in rapids, being less effected by crosscurrents and harder to submerge in waves or holes. Their forgiving nature is especially appreciated by beginners, and bigger folks who like the extra inside room. These designs are also preferred by many paddlers who attempt extremely difficult whitewater. Because big boats are less prone to pinning and more reliable in tight situations, they are preferred for steep, technical rivers.

A boat's depth at center is a pretty good indication of its total volume. Deeper boats usually have well-rounded sides that will make bracing & rolling easier. Low volume boats, however, frequently have well-defined sharp "edges" resulting from the drastic lowering of the deck. These edges catch in eddylines and countercurrents, flipping the unsuspecting boater. Such boats are particularly hard for beginners to handle. Look at the distribution of the volume as well as the total amount. High buoyancy bows plunge less deeply at the base of steep drops, and tend to ride over waves and holes rather than punching through them. Additional volume behind the cockpit makes ferrying easier, and volume ahead of the cockpit is helpful when surfing waves. Small volume boats plunge deeply when surfing, which if you enjoy enders can be quite exciting. In general you can say the smaller the boat, the more it is effected by the water, and the greater the emphasis on strength and skill.

For a number of years now there has been a trend to lower-volume boats, led by racers looking to improve their scores by "ducking" under slalom poles with their bow and stern. These boats can be surprisingly quick and responsive, and are ideally suited to smaller paddlers and juniors who would otherwise have a lot of trouble with the weight and bulk of a C-1 or kayak. While many larger paddlers find the increased liveliness and instability an amusing challenge, the more extreme designs are almost impossible for a big man to fit inside, much less to remain comfortable for long periods. Personal preference plays an important role in making the final choice, and anyone in the market for a boat is well-advised to try several boats until they discover the optimum size for their weight and style.

HULL SHAPE: Each canoe or kayak you see in the water represents a compromise between factors which enhance speed, maneuverability, and stability. Flat-bottomed, beamy boats are stable, but not very fast. Short hulls with upturned ends are quite maneuverable, but extremely sluggish. Narrow hulls with a deep, vee-shaped keel are speedy, but hard to turn or keep upright. Lets see why this is so, and how this effects the design of white water boats.

Its not hard to understand why a boat becomes more stable as it gets wider. As contact with the water broadens, the hull becomes more resistant to capsizing. The disadvantage, though, is that in a very wide, flat bottomed boat (such as an inflatable raft) stability ends abruptly when the boat lists to one side. Since river rapids can flip huge boats without trouble, you want a hull which will respond to the leans, braces, and rolls needed to stay upright and to recover from capsizing. The ideal whitewater hull shape,then,is full rounded, with a slight flattening of the bottom for stability. Beware of the ignorant but well-meaning dealer who tries to sell a beamy "river pig" because "it's soooo stable". While ideal for an elderly lady on a Sunday jaunt, such "cruising boats" are not responsive to modern techniques. An aggressive beginner will quickly become frustrated by his inability to perform, and will pass on the craft to another unsuspecting novice and move on to more exciting designs.

A true modern "cruiser" is designed for speed, and speed means a vee-shaped hull. Since a canoe or kayak with this hull shape sits on its keel, rather than its bottom, keeping it upright becomes something of a balancing act. But except for the fine-tuned racing designs, learning to use one is a lot like riding a bicycle. It's a bit nervous at first, but you'll catch on quickly after a few spills. The various designs on the market run from "shallow vees" which are a lot like ordinary designs to those which are "assymetrical","flared", and in every way similar to a racing machine.

Maneuverability is equally important, and this is determined by the length of boat which is actually in the water. The shorter the waterline length, the less resistance there is to turning. Because most kayaks and decked canoes are of about the same length, this characteristic is controlled by the lengthwise curvature of the hull, or "rocker". A kayak with "high rocker" turns quickly, but requires considerable skill to "track" in a straight line. The reverse is true for the sleek, "long-in-the water" designs with little rocker; such boats track effortlessly, but turn with great reluctance. Most cruising designs stay away from either extreme, combining high rocker with a vee-shaped bow or a very shallow full length keel. Such boats are ideal for beginning and expert whitewater paddlers.

Most of these flat-bottomed, round-sided hulls are what the racing set calls "pushers"; they kick up a large bow wake and require a lot of effort to paddle quickly on flat water. A narrow, tapered hull, with the widest part aft of center (an "assymetrical" or "swedeform" hull) cuts through the water much more easily, but is effectively narrower and therefore tippier. Wildwater, Marathon, and Olympic craft carry this trend a step further by "flaring" the sides so that the hull at the waterline is considerably narrower than the hull at its widest point, making the "profile" considerably sleeker. As these factors move to the extremes, the boats become much harder to handle. While a slick design means a lot in flat water, on a difficult river it can actually be a hinderance if you cannot keep it upright and steady enough to paddle hard.

STRUCTURAL CONSIDERATIONS are of no small importance to the home-builder. Vee-shaped fiberglass parts add rigidity; flat surfaces are more flexible. Since strength in a river boat depends on a hull flexing away from impact, vee shaped hulls are quite vulnerable to damage. But ridges can often add needed rigidity to decks, and several designers are known for this feature. But these convolutions are difficult to lay up, and some home craftsmen prefer to use internal reinforcement (discussed later). All sharp corners require extra reinforcement for long life, a step which many manufacturers do not take.

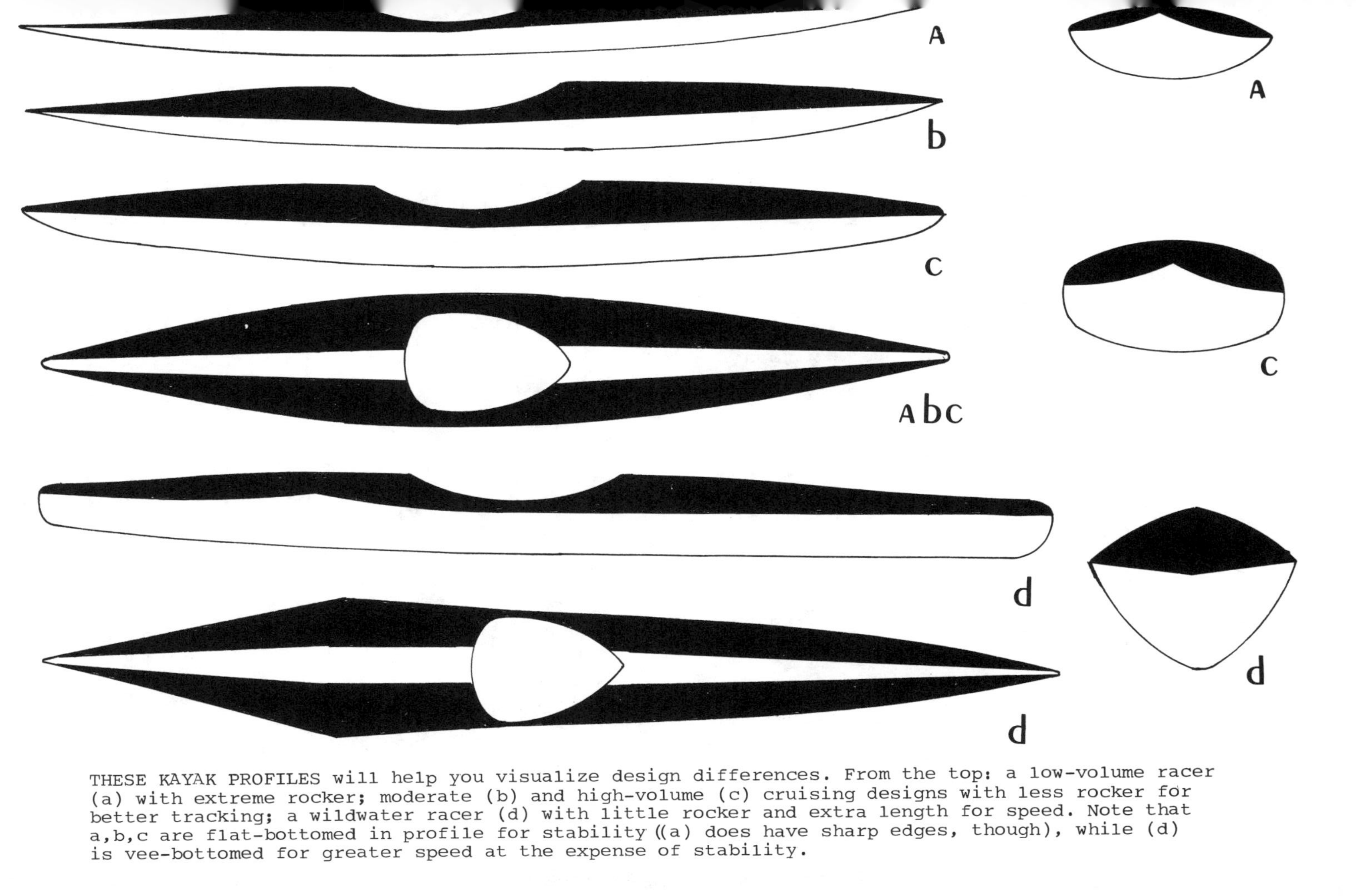

THESE KAYAK PROFILES will help you visualize design differences. From the top: a low-volume racer (a) with extreme rocker; moderate (b) and high-volume (c) cruising designs with less rocker for better tracking; a wildwater racer (d) with little rocker and extra length for speed. Note that a,b,c are flat-bottomed in profile for stability ((a) does have sharp edges, though), while (d) is vee-bottomed for greater speed at the expense of stability.

From Phoenix Products Photos

COCKPIT PLACEMENT: Weight distribution has a significant effect on a boat's handling qualities, as is shown by the way experts shift their weight when paddling. Cockpit placement is often critical; a few older molds have the opening in the wrong place. Some kayaks, like Dan Ruuska's "Outrage" kayak, feature adjustable seats which can be moved fore and aft. The seat can also be removed, a useful feature on overnight trips when gear must be carried along in the back. One advantage of homebuilding is that you can add features like this as you build. If your kayak does not "trim" properly fore and aft, it is advisable to move the seat. Low volume designs are particularly sensitive to weight shifts.

C-2's present a more complex problem: they must be trimmed to ride level despite significant differences in the weight of the people using it. This means that the cockpit openings must be individually adjusted for each pair; The correct technique involves making small cockpit holes, opening them up as needed to balance the boat. The new "center cockpit" designs are often (but not always) constructed with offset cockpits, bringing in the question of lateral trim and the decision as to whether to use a "bow right" or "bow left" configuration. Since several excellent teams do not use offset cockpits, the average person would be advised to simplify matters and do likewise. There is also the question of how close to sit; maneuverability increases as the boaters sit nearer to one another, but so do the problems of "paddle clashes" and the need for teamwork. The only way to successfully balance a doubles boat is in the water by trial and error experimentation. Do not install the rim or any fittings until this has been done. This also holds true for thwart placement in fine-tuned whitewater and marathon racing canoes, and with tandem wildwater craft.

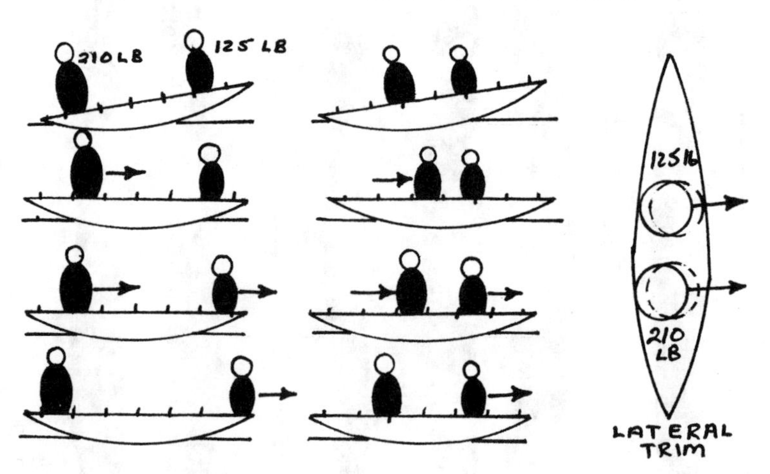

TYPES OF BOATS AVAILABLE:

Fiberglass canoes and kayaks fall into the following categories:

FLATWATER SPRINT: These "Olympic style" boats emphasize speed at the expense of everything else. They are not suited for rough water or untrained paddlers. C-1's are paddled from the "High-kneeling" position. Also includes the ICF Marathon boats, which are more extreme that American marathon designs.

DOWNRIVER, WILDWATER, and MARATHON RACERS emphasize speed, but make some concessions to stability and comfort. White water versions are high volume (for decked craft) or high-sided (for open canoes) for added seaworthiness and stability in rough water. Canoes are handled from a kneeling position. Marathon racing designs are less stable and quicker. Canoes are paddled from a seated position. This class of boat is not too maneuverable, and must be turned with a combination of strokes and offside leans. Not for the casual user.

TOURING: A boat designed for speed with enough stability and comfort for long-distance tripping and enough maneuverability for a person of ordinary skills to use it in mild whitewater. Although sometimes touted as an "all-around" design, it is not the best choice for someone interested in serious whitewater.

OCEAN KAYAKS are long-distance touring designs modified for ocean use. "British style" boats are narrow, fast, and tippy. "American" designs, produced primarily in the Pacific Northwest, are broader and more stable. Both are designed for speed with just enough maneuverability for landing in surf. They are usually made with watertight compartments, and feature hatches, high-backed seats, deck fittings, rudders, and other accessories.

CRUISING: These craft are designed for maneuverability and stability in heavy whitewater. Most are high-volume, with full-rounded sides, making few concessions to speed. The best of these designs were the "hot" slalom racers of the late 60's and early 70's, particularly those used in the 1972 Augsburg Olympics. Some lower-volume versions are also popular.

SLALOM RACING: The modern slalom design is extremely low volume, with incredible rocker for maximum maneuverability. When paddled casually, they do not track well, but under full power the stern buries, acting as a rudder for added speed. Many novices will find their extreme responsiveness more of a hazard than help, and big people (over 175 lbs) will find the inside room too small for comfort. But many folks, particularly those under 130 pounds, find them delightful as cruisers. Despite the added instability, many experts use them in big water for an added challenge.

SQUIRT BOATS are low-volume kayaks specially designed for three-dimensional "aquabatic" maneuvers. Many low-volume slalom boats will squirt, but the true "squirt boat" tends to be shorter and heavily reinforced. These designs are extremely sensitive to a user's weight and require a very high level of skill to paddle. Many are too small to be used safely by people weighing over 150 pounds.

JUNIOR BOATS: These are 3/4 size versions of decked boats for folks who weigh less than 100 pounds. The short length and low volume can be a liability in Class V water, but the usual occupant is a kid who "just can't wait" for a full-sized kayak or C-1. Parents with such a child will want him or her to have equipment scaled to their size, so that they can develop their skills with the least difficulty.

SHORT BOATS: Many paddlers, noticing that the ends of most white-water craft are out of the water, have chosen to try kayaks or C-1's which are between 1 and 3 feet shorter than standard slalom designs. The advantage is increased maneuverability and playability, as well as the novelty of learning to use a radically different boat. Such models track very poorly, and are ill-suited to flat-water travel.

SURF-YAKS are flat-bottomed, shovel-nosed machines designed for ocean surfing. They are designed to ride bow-high on the face of ocean waves for maximum maneuverability and control. Standard slalom kayaks are hard to turn, and tend to bury at the bottom of waves. The best designs are British, and the sport is well-developed there and in Australia.

SURF-SKIS are surfboards designed to be paddled like a kayak, The user holds himself onto the board with a seat-belt or some other device. These can be "swum out" through big breakers which whould flatten a kayak, then boarded and paddled back to shore. These are available through John Schriner's New Wave Kayaks.

ICF SPECIFICATIONS FOR WHITEWATER BOATS

Type of boat:	SLALOM: Minimum Length	WILDWATER: Maximum Length	BOTH:+ Min. Width
Kayak:	4.0 m/13.1'	4.5 m/14.8'	60cm/23.6"
C-1	4.0 m/13.3'	4.3 m/14.1'	70cm/27.5"
C-2	4.58m/15.0'	5.0 m/16.4'	80cm/31.5"

Boats competing in major races are checked to see that they conform to these specifications. CAUTION: since some molds are undersized, you can save youself needless hassle by checking your boat before arriving at the big event.

THE ETHICS OF COPYING:

The mold is the altar at which the paddler performs the rite of boatbuilding. The final shape of the craft which emerges is not accidental; but rather is the product of considerable effort on the part of the designer. While a few home craftsmen are also designers, most are not. They "pirate" an established design by "pulling" a mold off a successful commercial boat. For the designer, whose hundreds of hours of work made the project possible, such an act is considered theft. In essence he is right, but the matter is not so simple.

In the early 1960's, when decked boats first appeared on the American scene, it was virtually impossible to buy one. While there were a handfull of designers in the country, most of the kayaks and C-1's were descended from European racing designs brought over by the U.S. Whitewater Team. Competitors built molds for their own use, then rented them to recreational paddlers in order to recoup their expenses. Large club boatbuilding programs developed, many of which turned out 50-100 whitewater craft each year. Assistance in building a kayak was one of the benefits of membership. Most of the sport's participants were young and poor, and could not have gotten involved any other way.

By the early '70's the first significant commercial kayak fabricators were starting up. They purchased the rights to many of the same designs being used by clubs, and paid a stiff royalty on each kayak or canoe they made. Their main enimy was a network of backyard manufacturers, who sold their products for a fraction of the retail prices. But the distinction between these and the club programs was blurry, since many groups had members who would build to your order, but who paid no royalties. Charges and countercharges were exchanged. Lawsuits were threatened, and occasionally the matter reached the court. But the individual builder, put off by the poor quality and high costs of the commercial product, was not sympathetic. So the controversy continued.

the matter reached the courts. But time and technology were destined to defuse the controversy.

At first the manufacturer was ill-equipped to compete with the homebuilder. Although they ran very efficient shops, the normal overhead associated with being in business, combined with the dealer's mark-up, made their product extremely. expensive. Most suffered from cost pressures, poor quality control, and other problems. But by the end of the decade that had changed. Rotomolding, beginning with the River Chaser and culminating in the Perception line, created a product no small-time fabricator could match. The boats, while heavy, are virtually indestructable, and this has opened up new rivers and techniques to the user. In addition, the youthful crowd of the beginning of the decade has gone "yuppie". They now have plenty of money to support their hobbies and not enough time to fool around with fiberglass. Except for a few old-timers, perfectionists, and curious do-it-yourselfers hardly anyone builds anymore.

But back to the original issue: the legal aspects of copying are clear. It is against the law to sell another person's copyrighted design without permission. As a practical matter, the copyright holder must bring action in the courts, and the cost of a suit effectively insulates thei individual builder and most club programs. While a semi-commerical operator who pirates the work of American designers (whose work is every bit as good as the Europeans now) is in jepardy, most are sophisticated enough to modify the designs they steal ever so slightly to frustrate prosecution. "New designs" like this are common in the fashion industry, which has been unable to control such activity despite the huge sums of money involved. An extra button or lowered collar creates a good facimile of the latest designer "look", and is quickly copied in the Orient and rushed to the consumer. The increased popularity of rotomolded kayaks, however, has put most of the small-time pirates out of business.

There is, however, a moral side to the question, and that is that the designer deserves compensation for his or her work. It is clear that to facilitate this, mechanisms need to be available for the copyright holders to licence individual builders. Most of the larger companies with their imported designs are not interested in this; however, American designers are more pragmatic and flexible. But the bottom line is that the history of the mold and its design may not be known to the individual builder. I have been lucky in that all the molds I have used have been legal, with an arrangement between the designer and the mold owner. But when the designer will not negotiate, the potential builder must weigh the ethical considerations against the possibility of getting caught. My advice is to do all you can to assure that the designer gets his due, and to substantially modify any hull which you want to use, but cannot get permission to copy.

BACKGROUND INFORMATION: an overview of procedure

Before we get into all the details of building a canoe or kayak, it will be helpful to define our terms and outline the steps involved in the process. That way you won't get bogged down in details without understanding where each fits in. As all these steps will be described more fully later, don't worry if you can't quite visualize everything.

STEP ONE: MOLD PREPARATION: A mold is the boatbuilder's most essential and respected tool. It is made in two halves, like a seashell, joined along the sides of the canoe or kayak. Its rigidity is responsible for the shape of the deck and hull, while a smooth inner surface produces an attractive glossy finish. This surface must be maintained at all costs. Any cracks or other irregularities should be filled with body putty, and then polished with fine grades of wet sandpaper. The inside is then polished with wax, and treated with a release agent. This forms a barrier between the boat and the mold so that the finished product can be easily removed.

STEP TWO: HAND LAY-UP: Once the mold is prepared, the inner surface is coated with a thin layer of resin: the gel coat, followed by successive layers of fiberglass and other types of cloth. Each is laid in place individually and saturated with resin. Resin by itself is brittle; the cloths reinforce the resin in much the same way as steel reinforces concrete, holding it together. This permits the construction of a thin, very strong hull. The resin is then allowed to harden, or cure. The edges of the hull and deck are trimmed flush with the mold. The two halves of the boat are joined with successive layers of resin-saturated fiberglass tape. The completed shell can now be removed from the mold.

STEP THREE: OUTFITTING: The cockpit rim, seat, and other fittings are made up and attached to the shell so as to fit the owner/builder exactly. Both ends of the boat are "poured" with a solid plug of resin; grab loops are attached; deck-supporting walls are cut and installed. This is by far the most time-consuming facet of boatbuilding, with a lot of painstaking work required.

GLOSSARY:

The best way to get into a new subject quickly is to learn its structure; the structure is contained in language. We present the glossary at this time to make your further reading simpler.

TERMS RELATING TO MATERIALS:

RESIN: A liquid plastic material which becomes solid when hardening agents are added to it. Often (incorrectly) used to refer to the entire mixture of resin and hardener after mixing, but before hardening. Many types available; boatbuilders use Polyester, Vinylester, and Epoxy.

CATALYST: A hardening agent which promotes the reaction needed to "set-up" or "cure" a resin without becoming a part of the finished product. It works by lowering the temperature needed to effect a cure, or by shortening the time required to do so. Resins which use catalysts will harden by themselves in time, which explains why all resins have a definite "shelf life" A catalyst is added in small, critical amounts which depend on the temperature of the workplace. Too much will shorten its working life so that it can no longer be used.

HARDENER: A material which, when added to a resin, forms a link between resin molecules and hardens the material. It is actually a "co-reactant", and becomes an integral part of the mixture.

FORMULATION: A system of components (resin, hardening agent, and any modifiers or promoters) assembled to produce a hard plastic with a given set of properties. Other considerations, such as working time, viscosity, and toxicity must also be considered. Resins used for contact laminating do not shrink, sweat, or give off foul by-products while curing.

MODIFIER: A material added to a formulation to improve either physical properties (such as flexiblizers) or handling qualities (such as thixotropes).

PROMOTER: A material added to a formulation to work with the catalyst in setting off the hardening reaction. Different promoters result in different physical characteristics and handling qualities.

VISCOSITY: A measure of the thickness of a liquid; the thicker a formulation, the harder it is to work into the cloth. (with most systems, a formulation which is "too thin" is not encountered) It is usually expressed as a CPS value, with 300 being close to that of maple syrup or thin polyester formulations, and 1000 or more being comparable to molasses and the more difficult epoxies.

THIXOTROPY: An "anti-sag" property which causes the resin to cling to vertical mold surfaces without running or puddling. This quality is quite different from viscosity; many thick formulations are not thixotropic and "sag" badly. A resin which is not thixotropic will also run out of a laminate before it cures, causing voids. Most systems must be modified to achieve optimum properties. It should be noted that some store-bought formulations are mixed primarily for a long shelf life, and can be both viscous and non-thixotropic at the same time.

FILLER: any material added to a resin system which changes its properties by taking up space within the finished product. Usually refers to fiberglass and other cloths, but can include thixotropes like cab-o-sil and stiffeners like microballoons.

LAMINATE: A resin formulation reinforced with several layers of cloth and set to cure in a mold. The order in which the layers are set down and saturated is known as the layup.

MATRIX: A term for the cured resin within the finished laminate.

CLOTH: A material made up of woven strands of various synthetic fibers to be used in laminatintions with various resins. The standard of comparison is 10 oz Fiberglass cloth. The weave of the fabric (more so than its material) determines 1)how much resin is needed to achieve full saturation (tight weaves require less) 2) how difficult it is to achieve saturation (open weaves trap fewer air bubbles) and how well it will conform to sharp curves within the mold (again, an open weave is easier to work with) The weave also helps to determine the strength of the finished product; in some cases a more "difficult" weave is tolorated because of its superior performance in the finished laminate.

ROVING: An untwisted cord made from long strands of a given fiber. (Similar in appearance to binder's twine) May be woven into a heavy cloth (woven roving), chopped and fed into a spray machine, or wound around a plug. It is occasionally used for reinforcements on paddles and other items.

UNIDIRECTIONAL CLOTH: Cloth woven so that 60-98% of the fibers run lengthwise, with the crosswise fibers barely holding the material together. Used for selective reinforcement when the stress comes from only one direction.

MAT FABRIC: Randomized short fibers compressed into a cloth. Cheap, easy to work with, absorbs considerable resin. A boat built with this material would be heavy and brittle. Used extensively in building flatwater craft (where stiffness is important and light weight less so) and in the building of molds. Occasionally used in small quantities for patching and outfitting.

PIGMENT: A coloring agent mixed in with the resin used in both the gelcoat and the first layer of a boat. In addition to its aesthetic qualities, it protects the laminate from the effects of ultraviolet radiation (sunlight) which can over time turn a boat brittle. The main disadvantage is the contamination of the resin which occurs when excessive amounts of pigment must be used. This is not a problem with good-quality products, since a little goes a long way.

FINISH: A chemical coating or treatment given to cloth fibers (such as fiberglass) which do not ordinarily adhere well to resins. The resin will adhere to the coating which in turn attaches itself to the cloth. Most finishes are compatable with all systems; a few, however, are more specific. As most are water soluable, all fibers need to be protected from moisture.(the reason people who tried to build whitewater craft out of fiberglass curtain material failed was because the material was not finished correctly for their application.) Experimentation requires considerable knowledge and some risk !

COMPATIBILITY: A determination as to 1)Whether all components of the resin system will be completely utilized in the hardening reaction, becoming permanent parts of the finished product and 2) whether the resin system will bond effectively to the filler or fiber being used. This is primarily a problem faced by a manufacturer's R&D section; however, innovative boaters who are experimenting in new areas or using exotic materials need to be aware of it. An engineering background is helpful, but be aware that these folk DO NOT have all the answers. Also be aware that many "technically undesirable" combinations have worked out well in actual use.

TOXICITY: The danger which a component or combination thereof poses to human tissue. Dangers include: contact irritation (skin and eyes); contact sensitization; respiratory danger; skin absorption, and storage difficulties. See chapter on Safety.

TERMS PERTAINING TO PROCEDURE AND TECHNIQUE:

WET OUT: To saturate the cloth with resin. The tool normally used is a SQUEEGIE or plasticator available from auto body supply houses. (This is not to be confused with a window-washer's tool. You can make your own by cutting up polyetheylene (rubbermaid) dish pans. The larger sizes are best for applying resin to wide areas) Rollers and paintbrushes can also be used.

FORMULATING: Mixing a resin system, a task requiring varying degrees of skill and attention, and a lot more time than might be expected. The variables are: the pot size, the number of components in the system, and the accuracy required. If a system must be measured by weight, a scale accurate to the nearest 0.1 gram must be used. Volumetric measurement is faster, and for small quantities a syringe is indispensable (also "potting").

GEL TIME: The time required for a system to solidify in the mold. Once it has "set up," the resin will still be sticky and easily damaged. The mold can be moved without damaging its contents; however, the laminate should be kept warm and protected from moisture. A practical, not technical, definition.

CURE TIME: The time required for the resin system to harden to maximum strength. A minimum temperature of 60-70 degrees is usually required, there are exceptions with agents designed for low temperature cure. Some systems, particularly Epoxies, require a <u>heat cure</u> (over 85 degrees) for best results. Such systems require access to a specially designed oven. It is best to follow the manufacturer's curing schedule precisely, and to NEVER remove a boat from its mold until it is adequately cured.

END POUR: A solid plug of resin, filled with sawdust, microspheres, chopped fiberglass cloth, or other suitable material and forced into the end of the boat. Serves as a grab loop anchor, bow and stern seam sealer, and additional reinforcement for this inaccessible and vulnerable spot.

WORKING TIME: (Pot life): The length of time that a system can be worked after mixing. What usually happens is that the resin, prior to gelling, becomes too thick to use; the time this takes depends on the handling characteristics of the resin system in use and the size of the batch being mixed. A large batch has a smaller surface to volume ratio, and holds the heat of the hardening reaction better than a small one. As a result, the reaction procedes more quickly as the heat builds up. ANY batch will gel and cure faster than it will "laid up" in a mold. With some systems, the heat generated is so intense that the pot will "go off" suddenly in a cloud of foul-smelling vapors.

HOT MIX: Used to describe a batch mixed with a lot of catalyst to minimize cure time. Must be worked quickly and effectively or resin will be wasted. Excessively "hot" mixes in excess of recommended mixtures may result in a lamination in which the matrix is excessively brittle. If pot life becomes too short and the system cannot be modified, you will have to lower the working temperature (a real problem in the summertime!).

TO POP A BOAT: To separate a finished boat from the mold, using minimum necessary force. Can damage both the boat and the mold if done incorrectly, so be careful!

TO SEAM A BOAT: To join the two halves of a decked canoe or kayak toether along the sides using overlapping layers of cloth tape. This obnoxious procedure takes place inside the boat, and the concentration of fumes and confinement which results is enough to drive otherwise sane people to purchase store-bought kayaks. Must be done carefully, as the seam is the weak point in any boat. An "outside seam" may be added for extra strength, but this alone is not enough.

GEL COAT: In conventional fiberglass manufacturing procedure, this refers to an initial layer of resin which is put down on the inside of the mold and allowed to gel because the cloth is laid in. Special "gelcoat" formulations are manufactured for this purpose, but they tend to be extremely brittle. This process is not used much by builders of whitewater craft. The term is also used (incorrectly) to describe the initial layer of resin put down in the mold before the cloth is laid in. This layer is <u>not</u> allowed to gel, and is thus <u>not</u> a gelcoat. Moldbuilders will use a true gelcoat, usually a "tooling gelcoat" made expressly for the purpose.

MOLD: A rigid, concave form in the shape of a boat which takes the form of two halves (deck and hull) joined along the sides (the seam). Molds for seats, cockpit coamings, and internal fittings may also be available. A good mold must have sufficient strength and rigidity to hold its shape; a glassy-smooth inner surface; a clean, tight, properly aligned joint where the two halves meet, and a positive method of joining the two halves together.

PLUG: (A male mold); a rigid object in the shape of a boat used to produce a mold. An ordinary kayak can be used if properly prepared (copying) or the form can be made from scratch (designing). Copying involves considerable work and a number of ethical considerations discussed earlier.The production of an original "plug" is incredibly time-consuming.

DIFFERENT BOATBUILDING TECHNIQUES:

HAND LAY-UP (Contact laminating): The most common technique for building canoes and kayaks, and the major one used by home craftsmen. Layers of cloth are put inside the mold and saturated in place with resin. The builder, using different applicators and much patience, tries to: 1) completely saturate the cloth 2)remove air bubbles 3) eliminate wrinkles and 4) remove excess resin. A tedious, time consuming procedure when done well.

SPRAY-UP: A mechanized version of the hand lay-up system in which fiberglass roving is fed into a chopper gun and sprayed into a mold. This results in a heavy, brittle boat similar to one built with fiberglass mat. Spray-up has been tried (without the chopped roving) to saturate cloth, but quality suffered and the idea was scrapped. It does allow for the precise mixing of components. The fumes, however, are truly horrible and must not be inhaled.

VACUUM-BAGGING: An improved version of the hand lay-up technique in which a sheet of PVA plastic is placed over the laminate and sealed at the edges of the mold. Air is evacuated, the plastic film collapses, and pressure is applied to the laminate. This pressure allows air and excess resin to be easily evacuated, and for toxic resin systems to be worked with minimal worker contact. The problem is that as the system gets more complex, more things can go wrong. Leaks and pump failure are the greatest worries. (see below) Check chapter on vacuum bagging for more information.

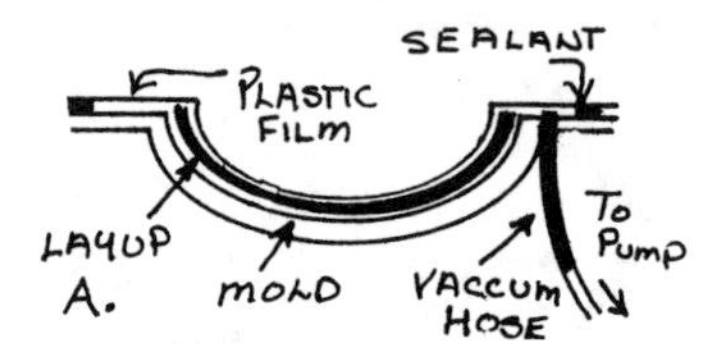

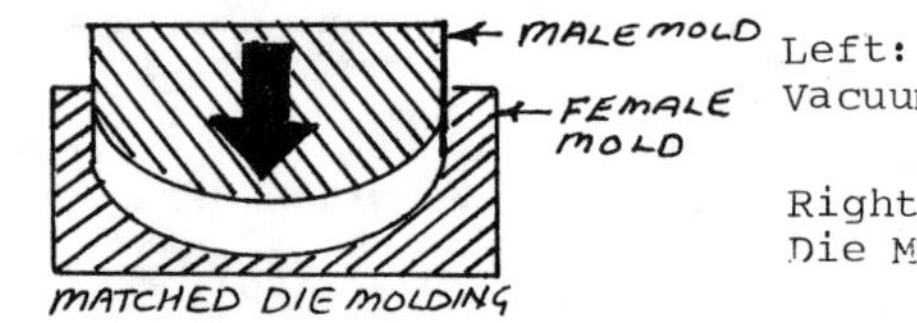

Left: Vacuum-baggi

Right: Match Die Molding

MATCHED-DIE MOLDING: This technique compresses the layup between matched molds to achieve complete saturation and to remove excess resin. Pressure is applied with a hydraulic press or (in ameteur applications) many C-Clamps. The biggest problem is that the molds tend to warp under stress, causing air bubbles. Applying pressure evenly is difficult. Norse and Illiad Paddles use this technique; the molds are too expensive and technically complex for building kayaks and canoes. (See above illustration & "Paddlemaking" Appendi

FILAMENT-WINDING: A high-technology, multi-step process which might result in a super boat. A plug is cast, and wrapped with a long, thin strand of the saturated roving of your choice in a carefully engineered pattern. The plug is then vacuum-bagged and heat cured. During the curing process, the mold melts and the material gathered and recast. The resulting craft is seamless. The pipe-dreaming of frustrated aerospace engineers.

VACUUM-FORMING: A technique in which a sheet of plastic is heated and placed over a mold. Air is evacuated, and the now-malleable sheet slips into place. Easier said than done, though. Used to produce Royalex and Royalite (TM) ABS boats.

ROTO-MOLDING: In this procedure, a powdered plastic is added to a specially-designed, heated mold. As the mold is rotated, the plastic melts and adheres to the inside. The result is a seamless, tough boat made from something a lot like Tupperware. A bit flexible, but tougher than fiberglass and thus very popular. Matched nickel-plated molds are a bit out of reach of the average paddler. Perception Kayaks are made this way.

TERMS RELATING TO QUALITY CONTROL:

CLOTH TO RESIN RATIO: The percentage of a laminate, by weight, occupied by cloth as compared to resin. Too much resin produces a heavy,brittle boat; too little results in a weak, leaky one. Each cloth has a different amount of resin which is absorbed to best advantage; fiberglass tends to take in a bit too much Kevlar a bit too little. The idea is to get the optimum ratio.

> RESIN STARVED refers to an area of cloth which contains too little resin. The cloth will appear light-colored and porous. The laminate here is weak and easily broken. Often caused by over-aggressive squeegie work.
>
> RESIN FLOODED: An area containing more resin than needed to saturate the cloth. This area will be stiff and brittle. It is often seen as a "puddle" in the bottom of the boat.

Both problems can be caused by inadequate thixotropy. The resin will run out of the sides, forming a puddle at the bottom and starved areas along the seams.

PINHOLES are tiny interconnecting air bubbles which occur when the cloth is not completely saturated. Invisible except under close examination; often found when a boat leaks inexplicably. May be caused by a overly viscous system, inadequate thixotropy, or gasification of the system during vacuum-bagging. Can often be sealed semi-permanently by multiple coats of paste wax.

AIR BUBBLES are pockets of air trapped between layers of cloth during lamination. Small ones are almost inevitable; larger ones can be removed by a careful builder. All weaken the bond between the layers and must be eliminated if possible. Most common with viscous resin systems and tightly woven cloths.

DELAMINATION: The separation of the layers of a boat due to impact, extreme flexing, or fatigue. Impact may shatter the resin between and within layers allowing them to separate. Extreme flexure causes extreme stress between the different layers (interlaminar shear) which causes them to separate. Fatigue, though not usually a problem with composites, can sometimes be seen in a brittle or improperly cured hull where polymer crosslinking is excessive. (As a result of too much catalyst, for example). The separating force is greatest at the center of the layup. Contributing factors include: differing degrees of flexibility between layers; lack of adhesion between layers due to resin starvation, differing rates of expansion and contraction in high temperatures, incompatability between resin and cloth, and sloppy craftsmanship. Some materials simply do not bond well to any resins; avoid using them in the center of a layup.

PATTERNING: If the"gelcoat" is too thin or the cloth used is too coarsely woven, the weave pattern may show through. Can also show through if air bubbles are not removed. Bad for boats; disaster for molds ! Most common location is in the bow or stern or at the peaks of ridges.

ALLIGATORING: A scaly pattern which appears in the outer (gel) layer of boats due to a) the infusion of styrene into the resin as a result of an excessively fast cure or b) thin spots in the gel coat. Avoid high-temperature work and excessively hot batches of resin, and make sure that the gel layer is applied thickly and uniformly.

CRAZING: Cracks caused by impacts which fracture the resin or cloth in the middle layer, leaving the outer layers undamaged. Visible as a white streak in clear & translucent boats. Weakens the laminate; may or may not cause leaks; can allow water to infiltrate between the layers causing extensive delamination.

SPLIT, BLOWN, or POPPED SEAMS: When the two halves of a boat become traumatically separated (partially or totally) due to violent mistreatment by various features of riverine geology, excessive deck pressure resulting from powerful hydraulic forces encountered during pop-ups and enders, rough or careless car-topping, sloppy craftsmanship. A real pain to repair properly, so it pays to over-engineer the seams when building.

A CLEAN RELEASE: What happens when the boat you're making is easily popped from the mold. If properly prepared, a mold will give up a boat easily. If not, the process may go a full fifteen rounds, with damage to the boat and mold probable.

WARPING: Distortion of the original shape of the boat caused by overexposure to heat or premature removal of an uncured boat from the mold. Every system has a HEAT DISTORTION TEMPERATURE, abbreviated HDT. Try to get a system with an HDT of $130-150^{+}$ degrees so you won't have summer woes.

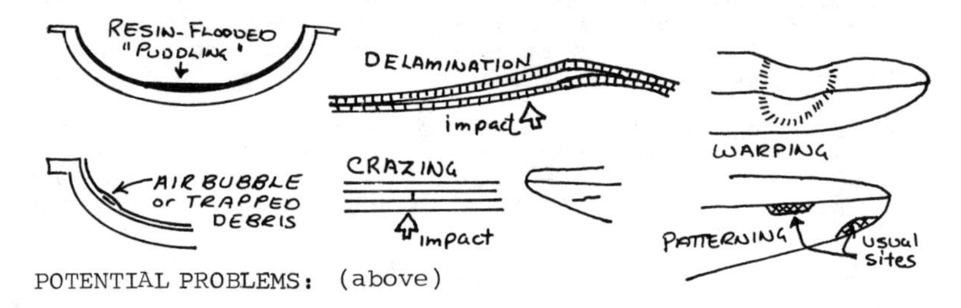

POTENTIAL PROBLEMS: (above)

STRENGTH, WEIGHT, AND COSTS: CHOOSING THE RIGHT LAYUP:

Much of the information contained herein comes from a master's thesis written by Chip Queitzsch for the Department of Civil Engineering at the University of Virginia, Charlottesville. Chip is a former U.S. Team member with extensive boat building experience, and he graciously took the time to design his thesis around my needs and to explain many of the concepts contained herein. It is hoped that this section will be readable as well as scientifically correct; however, some simplification of advanced concepts has been inevitable.

A Whitewater boat will, during its lifetime, be subject to many types of stresses including: uniform hydrostatic loading (sitting in flat water, point-impact loads (hitting a rock), transient hydrostatic loads of moderate intensity (punching waves and holes), high-intensity hydrostatic loads (playing holes; doing enders), and high-speed wind loads (from cartopping). In addition, there is the general abrasive wear and knocking about associated with rough handling. Normal engineering procedure involves determining the maximum stresses an object will undergo and designing a structure which has a substantial built-in safety margin. This works well for bridges, but nobody has to carry a bridge anywhere. A kayak so designed would be impossibly heavy. Since all whitewater layups are substantially under-designed, each boater must decide for himself how the necessary compromises should be made.

STRENGTH, WEIGHT, AND COST are closely related to one another. Decisions taken to improve performance in one area ultimately effect all others. Furthermore, improved performance in one area is often directly opposed to good results in another. Any boatbuilding technique is at best a good compromise, held together by the skills of the builder. This process of selection and compromise has been made easier by the development of certain high-cost, high technology materials which maintain strength while reducing weight. But many of these components place greater demands on the builder's abilities.

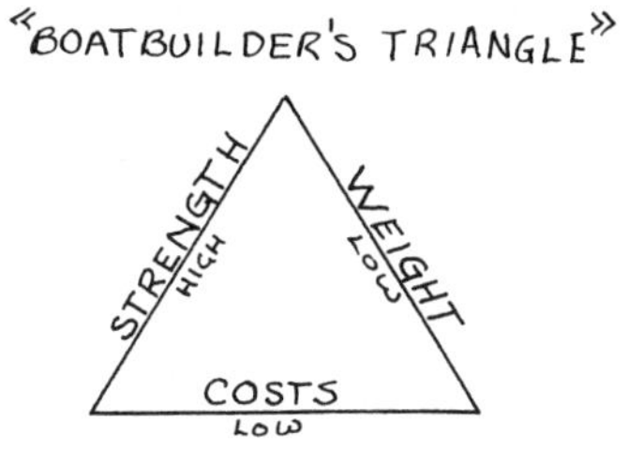

REMEMBER: A GOOD CRAFTSMAN WILL GET BETTER RESULTS WITH CONVENTIONAL MATERIALS THAN AN INEXPERIENCED ONE WILL FROM THE MOST EXOTIC COMPONENTS!

A DISCUSSION OF "STRENGTH"

In dealing with physical properties, nothing is as simple as it seems. Take the concept of "strength". We can define strength as the maximum stress that can be tolorated in a given material without failure. To a materials scientist, "failure" appears at the "first yield" of the material. This is a point when the material appears undamaged to the casual observer, but has begun to deteriorate nonetheless. What most whitewater boaters mean when they talk about failure is something more extreme: a torn laminate, ie: a rip, hole, or crack. Although the trauma can come about in various ways, all forces acting on the hull and deck can be broken down into three types of stress, as follows:

COMPRESSION AND TENSION: These two forces are best visualized if you think about what happens when you try to break a stick over your knee. As the "load" (knee pressure) is applied, the outside of the stick is in tension (being pulled apart) and the inside is in compression (being pushed in). When a rock hits a boat, the same thing happens to the laminate: the inner layer is in tension, the outer layer in compression. Since all materials are not equally good in tension and compression, it pays to locate them where the best qualities can be put to use and their weaknesses minimized.

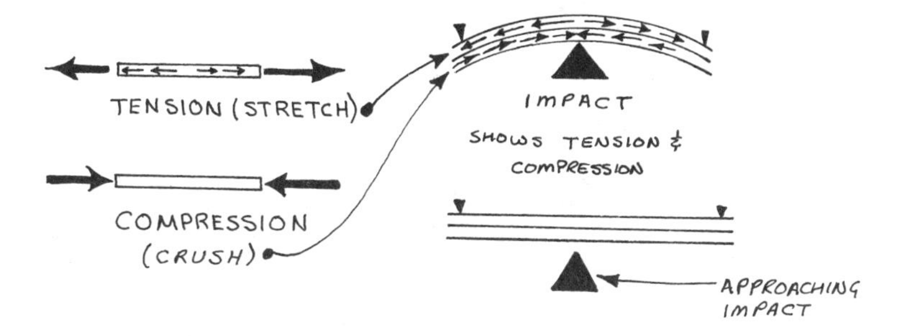

SHEAR STRESS comes in two forms: Interlaminar and Transverse. Each one creates its own set of problems, and must be discussed separately.

INTERLAMINAR SHEAR develops when a laminate flexes under impact or stress. With the outer layer in compression, and the inner layer in tension, the individual layers would like to creep past each other. The pressure to do so is greatest at the center of the laminate, and what stops it from happening is the resin bond between the layers. If the stress is great enough, however, the bond will fail and delamination results.

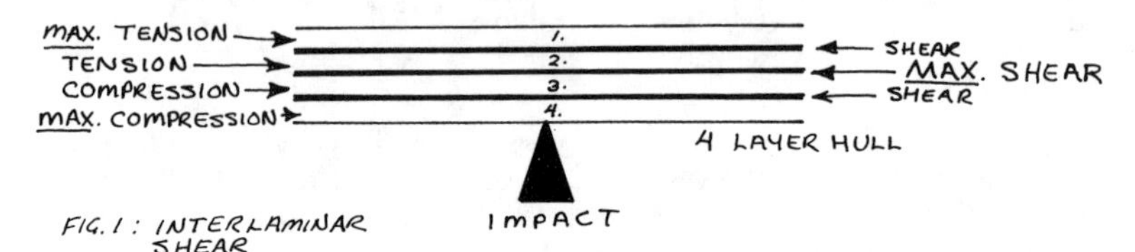

FIG. 1: INTERLAMINAR SHEAR

Two areas of a canoe or kayak are particularly vulnerable to delamination: 1) large, nearly flat "panels" with little inherent stiffness (such as the bottoms of open canoes) and 2) Vee-shaped keels and deck stiffeners which increase shear stress by concentrating it at the point of the vee. The former can be stiffened by ribs or carbon fibers to reduce the flexing that leads to damage without adding a lot of weight. Keels and deck ridges can be reinforced, but this is seldom completely effective. Fillers such as Cab-O-Sil and microbaloons can, when mixed in proper proportion, can greatly increase interlaminar shear strength by increasing the strength of the resin bond. Polyester and many synthetic reinforcements bond poorly; people using polyester are thus advised to avoid using synthetics in the center of the layup.

TRANSVERSE SHEAR can best be described as a concentration of stress across the laminate as a result of opposing forces, or loads. The result is a cutting action analagous to that of a pair of scissors ("shears"). There are two ways that this can happen: 1)contact with a sharp-edged rock focuses stress along its edge, and results in a well-defined hole in the hull with surprisingly little impact and 2) sudden or cumulative damage along a boundary between relatively rigid and flexible areas of a laminate. These boundaries are known as stress risers because stress and subsequent damage tends to be concentrated here.

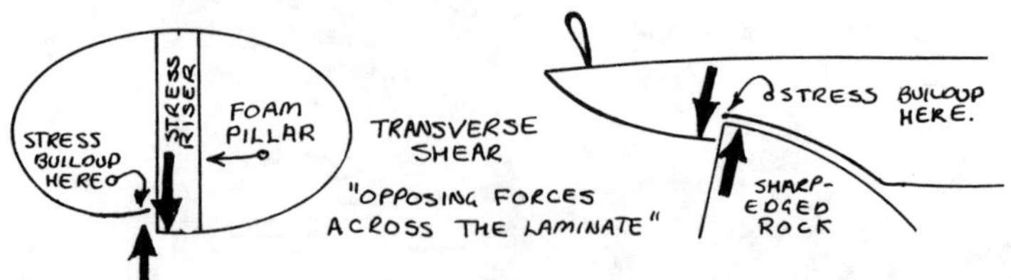

It is important for builders of white water boats to do what they can to avoid creating stress risers. Foam pillars are used in preference to more rigid materials such as plywood because it "gives", absorbing some of the impact. Overlapping seams and reinforcements are used to make thickness changes more gradual, minimizing the buildup of shear stress. Details of these techniques will be discussed fully later.

WHY WHITEWATER BOATS BREAK:

By now you may be starting to see why the goal of building an indestructable whitewater craft has proven to be so elusive to the nation's best builders. But much can be learned about how to prevent damage by understanging why these boats break up. Indeed, for most of us, the well-worn products of our shops has been our most demanding instructor, as well as our best source of new ideas. Often things which look great on paper do not hold up in practice, and ideas which seem illogical prove themselves long before we understand why.

There are two types of laminate failure of interest to whitewater boatbuilders: brittle failure and ductle failure. Brittle failure is the result of a "sudden and catastrophic" elongation; the layup cannot give, and must break under the impact. In a ductile failure, the damage is much more gradual. The hull can absorb substantial punishment without breaking, and although there is considerable internal damage, the boat remains watertight. The Marlex material used in roto-molded kayaks is a perfect example of a ductile material, as is the tupperware to which these boats are often compared. China is a brittle material, as are any canoes or kayaks constructed entirely of fiberglass.

The graphs below show the difference between brittle and ductile failure. The area under the graph represents the amount of energy absorbed prior to failure. Notice in a brittle material the ultimate strength and breaking strength are the same; this is not the case with a ductile material. In reality, most laminates have both brittle and ductle characteristics. In the laminates studied by Chip Queitzsch (but not all materials), the higher the ultimate strength, the stiffer the laminate and the greater the area under the propagation energy curve (past the "ultimate strength) the stiffer the layup will be after failure, and the more useful the material will be to the paddler.

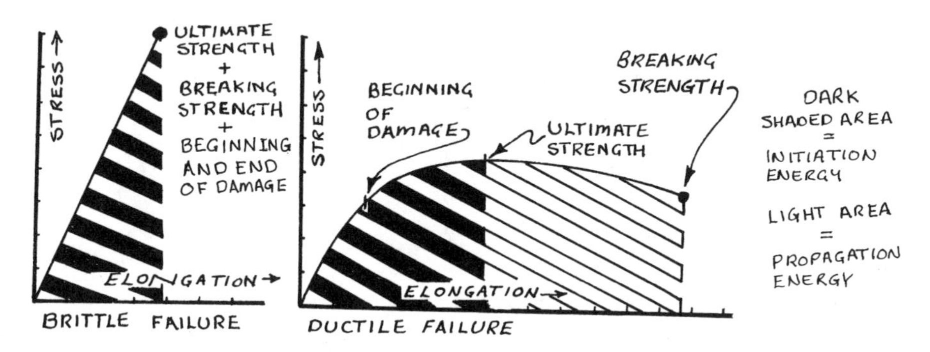

RIGID VS FLEXIBLE BOATS:

From a standpoint of performance, a rigid hull is much more desirable than a flexible one. The better a canoe or kayak holds its shape, the more likely it is to perform as the designer intended. However, it is impossible to get a rigid hull without also getting a brittle one. A laminate with the ductility needed for durability is going to be flexible. The flat water racer, for whom hull performance is of overriding concern, will put up with a fragile craft The whitewater paddler must seek a compromise between this and something so flexible as to pose a safety hazzard or which is simply unsatisfying to use.

Materials used for building white water craft fall into one of two categories: Fiberglass (E-Glass and S-Glass) and synthetics (Nylon, Polypropylene, Kevlar, CAP). An all fiberglass layup is quite rigid, and holds its shape well. It is however, a brittle substance, prone to sudden failure. Synthetics are more ductile, and can withstand more punishment without breaking. But used alone, they have problems. First, any flexing of a laminate causes subtle, invisible damage which accumulates as fatigue over the long haul. To understand how this works, lets go back to the knee over the stick analogy. If you bend the stick over your knee until internal cracking is heard, then back off, the stick appears undamaged. But wood fibers have broken (you heard them) and the stick's strength has therefore been reduced. The second problem is that excessive flexibility hurts performance. We have already spoken of hull deformation; the more serious problem is that of entrapment. An excessively flexible hull can collapse in a pinning, trapping you inside. Internal bracing can alleviate, but not eliminate, this problem. Lastly, all synthetic layups are subject to heat distortion (they melt on your rack if left in the sun !!) In many cases, the resulting damage is irreversable. For this reason, all modern fiberglass kayaks and canoes are composites of fiberglass and synthetics. Properly placed, each covers the deficiencies of the other to create a material tougher than the sum of its parts.

HOW MUCH WEIGHT:

No one has to ask why light weight is desirable for canoes and kayaks, particularly in white water. A lightweight hull responds more quickly to paddle strokes, and is easier to carry when on dry land. All whitewater craft, however, are under-designed, and light weight versions are cutting it even closer. There are a number of technical problems, which are not easily solved. Excessive flexibility is the biggest: a 25% reduction in hull thickness cuts its rigidity in half ! To avoid a significant reduction in performance, builders turn to high-technology materials and a complex system of internal supports. Needless to say, both of these approaches put an extra demand on the builder. In addition, when the hull becomes this thin, quality control becomes difficult. Air bubbles, pinholes, and other inconsistancies which might go unnoticed in a regular boat become real problems in a lighter one. There is also a significant loss of strength in a hull made with less materials.

DO YOU NEED A LIGHTWEIGHT BOAT ??

Considering the hassles involved when you attempt to produce a lightweight canoe or kayak, it is clear that the decision to do so must be made with care. The following factors could indicate that you'd be better off with a standard-weight product.

1) You weigh over 175 pounds: Heavy people are much harder on white water boats. The hull rides lower, and the added weight increases momentum for more serious impacts.

2) You run difficult whitewater frequently. This puts extra stress on a boat, particularly when the rivers are steep and technical rather than wide and powerful.

3) You run wilderness rivers, where you can't walk out easily and a battered boat becomes a serious problem

4) You're a hot dog: pop-ups, enders, big holes and nasty rapids make your day, and put extra wear on your boat.

5. You're cheap. Durability is important to you. You paddle a lot, and like to hold on to your boats for 3-5 years. before you sell.
6. You're a beginner. Beginners are particularly rough on boats, as they must make many mistakes to learn. If they are athletic and ambitious, this adds to the problem. A boat which can "take it" is much more conducive to learning than the latest lightweight design which will soon be covered with patches.

There are four types of folks who are better off with lighter boats:

1. The Expert: This is a paddler who does a lot of cruising and racing, and is willing to trade increased responsiveness and easier portaging for less durability. Knows how to avoid situations which could damage the boat .
2. The Tourist: prefers easier white water, is not particularly aggressive, and does not paddle frequently. Usually not anxious to advance to more demanding rivers, and thus does not need the extra margin that a heavier boat provides .
3. The Lightweight: weighs in at less than 120 pounds, and is thus conscious of weight differences more than a heavier colleague. Many female and junior paddlers fall into this category, and will not reach their potential without a low-volume, light weight boat.
4. The Racer seeks ultimate performance at the expense of everything else. Trades in his or her boat frequently, so durability is not at issue.

The advantage of light weight is greatest in slalom, where a paddler puts his boat through a series of sudden starts and stops, fighting inertia at every turn. Although there are considerable variations in body weight, this weight is concentrated amidships, where it can do the least damage. You'll notice the extra weight particularly at the ends. A ten-pound reduction is noticeably livelier even to novices, and has some significance to everyone. But a reduction of a pound or two, particularly the last pound or two, is of much less significance. The last few pounds are even less noticeable in wildwater, where durability is important and inertia has a certain advantage in itself. Suffice it to say that there is an optimum weight for each use, and that the technical problems involved in going lower are not justified by the results.

A river runner notices weight more at the put-in and take out than on the river. For him, durability is the key, and that goes double for those who get way out into the back-country to run their hair. Abrasion and impacts are much more severe than in racing, and hydraulic pressure from pop-ups and enders can be too severe for all but the toughest boats. With toughness comes a certain amount of extra weight. How much depends on your choice of materials, and the skill of the craftsman.

The beginner, despite what some people may say, does not need the snob appeal of a lightweight boat. He needs a strong boat which can stand up to the mistakes that he'll have to make to learn to paddle. After a suitable apprenticeship, he'll be ready for a light boat, and that boat will last for years. The advantage of home-building is that you can build exactly the boat you need; one which will give maximum enjoyment on the river. There is no need to be stuck with a "river pig;" careful choice of materials and a bit of care, a 35-pound boat can be as durable as one weighing in at 50 pounds plus ! The extra weight really is noticeable, and is worth getting rid of even if you never plan to race. Knock off another 15 pounds for racing.

How much "weight" are we talking about? With canoes and kayaks varying so much in size and volume, its difficult to give precise figures. But we can say that 30 pounds for a medium-volume kayak; 35 pounds for a medium-volume C-1; 45 pounds for an end-hole C-2, and 55 pounds for a 15' open canoe is about "average". Racers can reduce these weights by 15-30 per cent, depending on materials. a "small volume" boat starts 15-20 per cent lighter. There is some question as to whether the increased vulnerability is worth the weight loss in slalom. Wildwater racers and most river runners already feel it is not. But on the other hand, you don't need a "river pig" which runs as much as 50% over the norms. These are seldom enough stronger to justify the extra energy needed to muscle it around.

ADDITIONAL PROBLEMS:

PLASTIC DEFORMATION is caused when a material is stretched beyond its elastc limit without breaking, resulting in permanent residual deformation even after the stress is moved. Some plastics recover better than others, but usuallv a boat which has been "wrapped" around a boulder will be permanently disfigured.

HEAT DISTORTION can come about as a result of intense summer heat combined with steady pressure. Roof racks, tie downs, and a hot summer sun are the usual culprits. Synthetic cloths are more than a little vulnerable to this problem; fiberglass laminates less so. Most hassles can be avoided by making certain that the materials you use have a Heat Distortion Temperature of at least 130 degrees, and storing your boat out of the sun, with the hull well supported.

ABRASION is a long-term problem for boatbuilders, particularly those who attempt numerous streams at marginal water levels. The harder a resin, the greater its resistance to abrasive wear; the same is true for the cloth. Unfortunately, extremely hard systems tend to be brittle. The softer systems, being more flexible, can withstand more punishment. For this reason most builders use a rigid resin modified with a flexible one for optimum characteristics. The optimum mix is determined by experimentation.

As the outer shell of a boat wears, the cloth fibers become exposed. Fiberglass tends to "wear smooth", while the synthetics tend to become "fuzzy" when abraded. For this reason, many people prefer to keep synthetics inside the laminate; however, because this may lead to delamination in some systems (polyester resins) others have chosen to leave it out and put up with the fuzzing.

THE LOWDOWN ON COSTS:

A whitewater boat is a high-technology item. In them, as with most similar items, you are buying a lot of brainpower and that brainpower is expensive. Considering the "boatbuilder's triangle" again, let's examine some of the alternatives:

HIGH STRENGTH, LIGHT WEIGHT: Achievable only with advanced materials which are expensive and often difficult to obtain and use. In addition, toxicity is often a problem, and the extra care needed to be safe raises labor costs and is the main reason why most manufacturers will not go this route. Another option is to carefully reinforce standard materials, but this ups labor costs, too. Therefore:

HIGH STRENGTH + LIGHT WEIGHT = HIGH COSTS

HIGH STRENGTH, LOW COST boats can be achieved, say some, by using copious amounts of cheap materials. To a limited extent, this is true. Rigidity is a function of thickness as well as materials; a thick hull made from weak materials may perform as well as a thin hull made from stronger ones. But there are problems: a thick layup has low elongation (it is very stiff, and brittle), cracking under extreme pressures which would not faze a more flexible boat. And remember that this type of layup is not all that cheap, as labor time is about the same as before. Therefore:

HIGH STRENGTH + LOW COSTS = HEAVY WEIGHT (Strength doubtful)

LIGHT WEIGHT, LOW COST was first achieved by using small amounts of cheap materials (the Austrian 1-race throwaways of the 1960's) These boats were weak, and easily destroyed if anything went wrong. Slightly stronger versions were still plagued by problems of excessive flexibility, weakness, and pinholes in the layup. And again, these boats are not that cheap, because it still takes about the same time to build them. Therefore:

LIGHT WEIGHT + LOW COSTS = LOW STRENGTH (Savings doubtful)

The only logical way to go, therefore, is with the best materials you can possibly afford. Anything less is a waste of time and effort. The only reason to hold back is if you are not sure of your skills and want to build a "first boat" at minimum cost until you learn how to build effectively.

But materials costs are only part of the story. Even with labor (yours) supplied free, there are a number of "hidden costs" which must be added in.

Materials:	Hidden Costs:
Cloth: $90 - $200 (40 yds)	Mold Rental: $20-$50
Resin: $40 - $110 (3 gals)	Transportation: 20¢/mi.
Ethafoam: $25 (9 sq.ft.)	Shop expenses: $15-$30

The reasons for the variations include 1) simple vs. high-tech systems and 2) retail vs bulk buying. Add about $20 for vacuum bagging materials, plus whatever it takes to obtain the pump and associated plumbing. Prices as of late 1981 are sure to reflect soaring costs of all petrochemicals.

WARNING to group buying programs: do not sell at cost ! Add at least 10% to cover shipping, phone calls, and other overhead that inevitably comes up. This won't be enough to make a profit, but it will keep you from losing money on the deal.

EPOXY RESIN SYSTEMS:

Epoxy resins are considered to be the ultimate matrix for white water boats. A good system yields superior stiffness and strength, along with excellent hardness and abrasion resistance. Even the less sophisticated formulations produce a very tough (although a good bit more flexible) boat. There is a long list of problems which frustrate potential users, however. The first involves the difficulty of formulating a good system. Standard mixtures tend to be either too flexible or too brittle; the best are complex and require precise measurement. In addition, the components of any system are toxic, usually on par with poison ivy. Some special formulations are extremely dangerous. Epoxies demand careful mixing and handling for reliable results. Slobs will do more than just turn out crummy boats; they are a positive danger to their co-workers !

Epoxy systems are based on a thick, straw-colored resin known as DGEBA to which a broad range of modifiers, diluents, and curing agents may be added. The resin itself comes in a broad range of molecular weights, ranging from solids to thick liquids. Only the lowest molecular weights are suitable for boatbuilding, and many of these will require dilution to lower viscosity further. Most epoxies store well, but crystallize with age. Dust particles tend to "seed" crystals and work against the person who keeps a dirty shop. (This process can be reversed by warming the resin over mild heat) ALL RESINS ARE MILDLY IRRITATING TO THE SKIN, and must be handled carefully.

NB: Dow Chemical Co. recently came out with a DGEBF epoxy which is less viscous, but more expensive and harder to get.

DILUENTS are used to lower the viscosity of epoxies for specific uses.They have a number of disadvantages. First, their low molecular weight lends itself to easy evaporation and ready absorption through the lungs. These smaller molecules are also far more irritating to the skin than the base resin. Furthermore, diluents tend to reduce the strength of the resin by inhibiting the formation of the cross-linkages in the cured matrix. The major advantage of vacuum bagging is that it isolates the builder from these dangerous chemicals while at the same time permitting more viscous, less dilute resins to be used.

BGE (butyl glycital ether) is the most common diluent, and is mixed in most commonly available systems. CGE (Cresyl glycital ether) is less toxic than BGE, but also less effective, so that more must be used to gain the same result. It is occasionally found in premixed formulations. VDO (vinyl cyclohexine dioxide) is a very effective diluent which imparts excellent mechanical properties to a laminate It is also extremely toxic, and should be used by experienced builders only. Heloxy MK-116 (Monsanto Chemical) is a new safety diluent which cuts risk and works well, but greatly increases gel time unless an accelerator is added. Monsanto's MOD-EPOX is also quite good, but tends to come out of solution and cannot be premixed unless a stabilizer is added.

CURING AGENTS for epoxies are quite diverse, much more so than the resins themselves. They are the ones which determine the character of a system. Since the components must be used in stochiometric ratios so that all of the parts of a system are completely used up, a great deal of accuracy is needed in mixing. The diluent is an important part of the mixture; variations in type or amount will require an adjustment of the curing agent as well. Casual boatbuilders must be ready to follow instructions carefully if disaster is to be avoided.

The following general categories of hardeners are commonly used:

POLYAMIDES are the safest and easiest hardeners to use. They are less toxic and very tolorant of mixing errors. Adhesion is excellent (most "epoxy glues" are of this type) and thus they are well-suited for seaming, outfitting, and repair. The long gel time is inconvenient for mass production, but is a real plus for the conscientious builder. Large batches are safely mixed, and the extra working time more than makes up for the increased viscosity. (Hand layup is done with the least viscous resins; vacuum-baggers can move up to the higher numbers). A two-week room temperature cure or 12 hours at 130 degrees is needed to achieve full strength. Finished laminates tend towards flexibility. The system can be cleaned up with soap and water if you catch spills before they harden. RECOMMENDED FOR INEXPERIENCED BOATBUILDERS. Trade names of comparable hardners include: DEH-14 (Dow); V-40 (Shell) Versamid 140 (General Mills) and Polyamid 840 (Ciba-Geigy). Ideal for wet-layup vacuum bagging. (See notes 2-4)

PROPERTY	Resin: DER 321; DER 334	DER 332 **
PHR	43	43
Viscosity	2800	6500
Pot Life	210 Minutes	160 Minutes
Elongation	5% (most flexible)	2% (least flexible due to absence of diluent)

** Bag molding only. Too viscous for hand layup

PHR = Parts per hundredweight of resin. Translated: If a hardener is to be added at 43 PHR, take 100 grams of resin and add 43 grams of hardner for a total weight of 143 grams for the complete formulation.

This should not be confused with a 43 per cent mixture, which would mean 43 grams of hardener and 57 grams of resin for a total weight of 100 grams.

NOTE: Volumetric measurements cannot usually be trusted. However, they DO WORK with the above systems. For "fast and dirty" patching, a 1:1 ratio is OK.

ALIPHATIC AMINE SYSTEMS: the most commonly used hardener in this class is TETA. (DETA is also around). Like the polyamides, no heat cure is needed (although it will improve its properties). It is much less viscous than the above systems; it is easier to work, and yields superior mechanical properties. But beware: this system is a nasty, ill tempered bitch ! It is highly corrosive and toxic, has a very short pot life, and is incredibly intolerant of mixing errors. Combined with CGE-diluted resins, it weathers poorly and absorbs water. The finished laminate is far too brittle, and must be combined with a flexiblizer when working with undiluted resins. LP-33 is a commonly used polysuphide rubber flexibilizer. The LP-33 does not alter the viscosity of the resin, but it shortens the pot life outrageously. And if a pot "goes off", it gives off a foul-smelling brown gas which makes the whole neighborhood smell like an open sewer (NB-this gas is poisionous, too !). It is the opinion of the author that this system should not be used in hand lay-up, and is adaptable to vacuum bagging by experts only. Good for fast patching and outfitting, though !

PROPERTY:	Resin: DER 321	DER 331**	DER 332**
PHR	13.5	13	13
Viscosity	400	2200	9000
Pot Life	35 Min	30 min	30 min
Elongation	3.8%	4.4%	4.4%

** Vacuum bagging only

Suggested System for experts only: 80 parts #332 ; 20 parts VDO; 17 parts TETA. Very tough, but quite demanding for the builder. Caution is advised.

JEFFAMINE HARDENER: Jeffamine D-230 is currently extremely popular among experienced homebuilders. Its advantages include low viscosity, controllable gel time, versatility, non-critical mixing ratios, and excellent mechanical properties. No flexiblizers are needed with Jeffamine; however, the use of an accelerator, A398, is recommended to shorten an already overlong gel time. (If the resin takes too long to gel, it will run down the sides of the mold and puddle in the bottom.) The accelerator changes the properties of the cured laminate, and precise information on exactly how much is available from Jefferson Chemical. There are two disadvantages: first, Jeffamine is only slightly less toxic than TETA. It is quite corrosive, and capable of producing mild skin burns and very serious eye burns on contact. Also, since about twice as much is used to cure a comparable amount of resin as TETA, the mixture is equally toxic. Hand lay-up people had best take all possible precautions. Furthermore, Jeffamine is extremely slow curing, even with an accelerator. IT MUST BE HEAT CURED for 2-3 hours at 100-130 degrees C. before using, or it will fall apart ! A few people let Jeffamine sit a few hours prior to use as a way of decreasing its gel time. This increases viscosity, and improves its handling qualities, as otherwise it is a bit too thin.

PROPERTY	Resin: DER 331 & 332 w/ 35 PHR D-230	DER 331 or 332 w/ 30 PHR D-230 & 2 PHR A-398	DER 331 or 33 w/25 PHR D-23 & 5 PHR A-398
Viscosity	400	750	1200
Pot Life	300 min	121 min	58 min
Elongation	7.6%	7%	6.7%
Recommended use:	NOT RECOMMENDED Gel time 16 hr	Hand Layup Vacuum Bagging	Hand Layup Dry Bagging

Note: Increased amounts of Jeffamine increase laminate flexibility.
John Brown recommended formulation: 100 parts DER 331 or 332; 1 part DNP-30 enhancer; 25 parts D-230; 5 parts A-398.

CAUTION: Extremely adhesive resin. Will seep through small gaps in releases. Use plenty of wax and PVA, or purchase special release agents from your supplier.

Minimum Heat Cure: 2 hours at 180 degrees before any stress

TECHNICAL DATA by Steve Rock from manufacturer's literature and personal experience.

CAUTION: DERMATITIS, RESPIRATORY CONGESTION, AND OTHER ALLERGIC reactions, some of which may be quite severe, may result from prolonged exposure to the components in epoxy resin systems. The resins themselves are almost inert; the hardeners and diluents are all irritating and some are extremely toxic. Persons with a history of allergies may already be sensitive to epoxy, but everyone who comes in contact with these chemicals will inevitably have problems. In mild cases, this takes the form of a rash similar to poison ivy or slight respiratory congestion. IF THIS HAPPENS, STOP WORK IMMEDIATELY ! This is your first warning. Severe dermatitis, breathing difficulties, or impairment of vision may follow. Several people in the paddling community have been hospitalized as a result. Once sensitized, you can never work with epoxy without a reccurence of symtoms. Some people "break out" while sitting in an epoxy boat or entering a room painted with epoxy paint. But there is always the slob who sleeps in the stuff and never has any problems.

THE DANGER TO A CONCIENTIOUS PERSON TAKING PROPER PRECAUTIONS, though, is minimal. You're just going to be building a single canoe or kayak; most of the hassles result from really prolonged exposure. The idea is to minimize contact with the resin using 1) protective clothing which is impervious to resin 2) barrier cream on all exposed areas, particularly your hands and arms 3) Rubber gloves or equivalent 4) A respirator with the correct filter. Be careful about what you touch (ie your face and eyes) when building. Unless you are a part of an "at risk" group for epoxy sensitization, you should have little or no trouble so long as you take steps to minimize ANY CONTACT with the resin.

The following groups are especially at risk:

1) People with light complexions or sensitive skin
2) People with a history of allergies
3) People with a history of asthma
4) People who work with Epoxy Resin frequently

With the exception of group 4, these folks would be better off not using Epoxy resins when building a boat.

ADDITIONAL INFORMATION:

1. If an epoxy resin should become crystallized it can be brought back by heating it to 140 degrees F. in hot tap water. Just fill a large pot, and put the resin container inside. Since the diluent may evaporate, particularly with age, all resins should be tightly capped when not in use.

2. Preheating polyamide systems will reduce their viscosity and improve workability. This shortens pot life somewhat, but this can be minimized by preheating the two components separately prior to mixing. Use hot tap water, as above, being very careful to keep the water out of the resin pot.

3) A number of different hardeners can be added to polyamides to improve their mechanical qualities. AEP is a rather toxic material which, when diluted with a polyamide hardener, results in a laminate with high impact strength and other useful properties. Because of its toxicity and fast geling time, it is not recommended for beginners or for vacuum-bagging. The final laminate must be heat cured.

   TETA can also be mixed with polyamides,not so much to improve the mechanical properties as to effect a shorter room temperature cure. One worker has reported that the resulting laminate is much harder, and therefore more abrasion resistant. What most people do is add half the usual amount of polyamid hardener and half the usual amount of TETA

4) Epoxy diluents are actually very low molecular weight epoxies, and as such, effect the amount of hardener needed. While not essential, many experimenters will want to take these differences into account. See the Dow Chemical Co. Pamphlet "Dow Epoxy Resins" for information on how to compensate for variations in the amount of diluent in a given system. This is especially important if you must add diluent yourself to lower the viscosity.

5) Mixing large batches of resin made from components of varying viscosity can be very time consuming, and if the pot life is short, quite inconvenient. Mechanical devices, such as a paint mixer on a drill, are recommended

   Measuring quantities for mixing is by weight. If you decide to figure out volumetric equivelents, you'll need a syringe or pipette to accurately measure small amounts of hardner. Scales should be accurate to the nearest .1 gram.

THE TABLE on the following page gives some idea of the different epoxies available. Since most people with whom I keep in contact no longer use epoxy for boatbuilding, this information should be considered current as of 1979.

COMPANY AND TRADENAME	UNMODIFIED DGEBA RESINS: (Vacuum Bagging Only)			DILUTED RESINS MED. VISCOSITY BASE (for hand lay-up)	
VISCOSITY	LOWEST	LOW	MEDIUM	W/25% CGE	W/12%BG
SHELL "epon"	825 - 4-6K	826 180-188 6.5-9.5K	828 182-190 10-16K		815 175-195 500-700
DOW CHEM. "DER"	332 172-176 4-6K	330 180-189 7-10K	331 182-190 11-14K	321 182-192 500-700	334 176-186 500-700
CIBA-GEIGY "Araldite"	6004 178+ 5-6.5K	6005 175+ 7-10K	6010 185-196 12-16K	507 185-192 500-700	50 172-185 500-700
UNION CARBIDE "Bakelite"	ERL 2710 171-181 4-5K	ERL 2772 175-185 7-9K	ERL 2774 180-195 11-13.5K	ERL 2713 185-192 500-700	ERL 279 180-195 500-700
REICHOLD "Epotuf"		37-139 182-195 5-10K	37-140 185-200 10-19K		37-130 185-200 500-700
JONES-DABNEY Celanese "Epirez"	508 171-177 3.6-5.5K	509 178-193 7-10K	510 180-200 10-16K	5077 185-192 500-700	5071 180-195 500-700

HOW TO READ THIS TABLE:

Example given is for DOW CHEMICAL'S NEW DGEBF Epoxy, not listed above.

XD-7818	Resin System DESIGNATION
165	Epoxy Equivilent Weight(2)
3500	Viscosity, in CPS(3)

For explanation of numbers, see bel

1) Lowest Viscosity resins will crystalize easier than those label "low viscosity." Medium viscosity resins (and DGEBF resins) do not crystallize.

2) EEW=Epoxy equivilent weight - denotes the chemical reactivity o the resin, and how much hardener is needed.

3) Viscosity is measured in CPS; the higher the number, the thicke the resin.

4) DATA for this table was compiled by Steve Rock from Lee-Neville Handbook of Epoxy Resins and from company literature. Its purpo is to cross-reference available materials, and serve as a start point for experimenters. It is NOT all-inclusive.

POLYESTER AND VINYLESTER RESIN SYSTEMS:

Polyester resins have long been a staple of the reinforced plastics industry. Vinylesters are relatively new, and their superior toughness has earned them popularity among kayak and canoe manufacturers. Since they have many similar characteristics, they will be discussed together. Bear in mind that the mechanical qualities are quite different, as is their cost.

1. All of these resins eventually gel and cure on their own over several years time. Since most of us are too impatient to wait, two chemicals are added to speed up the reaction and to control gelling and curing.

The promoter activates the resin for use with the catalist, and in the process shortens the shelf life from years to months. Most resins are sold to the public pre-promoted, meaning that you might get material which must be used rather quickly. Try to purchase from a dealer with the high turnover needed to maintain fresh stock, or knowledgeable enough to add the promoter prior to sale.

The catalyst completes the job in an easily controlled manner, the gel and cure times varying directly with the amounts being used. The usual catalyst, methyl-ethyl-ketone-perokide (MEKP) is a volitile, flammable, thoroughly obnoxious chemical which can burn skin or eyes. It must be handled with great care; even the fumes can cause eye irritation !

CAUTION: Adding promoter and catalyst simultainiously will result in what is called "explosive decomposition". The two must be kept separate, and the catalyst not added until the promoter is thoroughly mixed. USE GREAT CAUTION!

2. Polyester and Vinylester are terms which refer to classes of resins. There is considerable variation within these classes, and most are too brittle for use in whitewater boats. The WORST POSSIBLE place to buy polyester resins is at a mass marketer like Sears or J.C. Penny's. Their product is formulated as a substitute for varnish; they promote it, then inhibit it for longer shelf life, dilute it with styrene to make it brush on easily, and keep it on the shelf for long periods. Horrible ! Most manufacturered formulations must be modified before use. Your best source is a person who sells the correct system especially for boatbuilding.

3. Polyesters and vinylesters require a curing temperature of at least 60 degrees; 70 degrees is preferable. Special promoters are available for low-temperature cures. Very hot summer temperatures (over 80 degrees) require special skills, as the reaction tends to move along very quickly unless you can adjust by reducing the amount of catalyst. Some vinlyesters require a heat cure because of the specific promoter being used. GET FULL INSTRUCTIONS FROM YOUR SUPPLIER.

4. Polyesters and vinylesters are air inhibited, which means that the surface does not cure fully, and remains tacky for some time. This is no problem for vacuum-baggers, since the inner surface is airless. Some builders find this property a pain and add tack-free-additive (TFA) to the mixture. TFA is a wax-styrene dispersion; as the material cures, the wax rises to the surface and keeps the air from the resin. As this degrades (weakens) the laminate somewhat, it should be added to the resin used in the final layer only. To attach any interior fittings (seams, cockpit rim, etc) the builder must sand through this wax layer. For this reason some builders do not use TFA, as it allows them to work on fresh layups without sanding. (This comment comes from J.R. Sweet)

5. Polyester and vinylester resins contain styrene monomer as a reactive diluent. This stuff is extremely flammable (flash point 90 degrees F) so you should take all reasonable precautions against fire. It is possible to thin

the resin with styrene, but this causes a number of problems, to whit: a) degrading the resin, making it more brittle and b) evaporating during the cure (when used to excess) causing pinholes. Since styrene will evaporate, resin stored for any length of time should be in tightly-closed glass or metal containers. Store in a cool, dry place, as exposure to temperatures over 80 degrees F will greatly shorten shelf life. Plastic containers are permissable only for short periods, as the styrene will evaporate through the container. Guard against contamination by dirt, water, and (especially) MEKP. A small quantity of catalyst can "set off" an entire drum in less than a week !

6. It is the opinion of the author and other experienced boatbuilders that the toxicity of both polyester and vinylester is greatly underrated. This particular tale comes from Stew Coffin, one of the earliest builders of whitewater craft in the entire country.

   "Looking back, I figure that the worst thing was styrene fumes. We did a bit of subsistance farming on the side, and at one time we dressed and ate a rabbit which had been brought into my shop for a short while prior to slaughter. The meat was badly tainted with styrene, especially the liver. More than one person has observed that certain people who worked polyester resin a lot tended to be edgy, and I have attributed this to styrene. It was not long after this that I gave up boatbuilding altogether."

   From a letter from Stew Coffin

OBTAINING THE PROPER POLYESTER:

Polyester is produced in both "rigid" and "flexible" forms. The "rigid" resin is too stiff and brittle; the flexible resin too soft and floppy. But mixed together in the proper ratio (between 3:1 and 6:1 rigid:flexible) you can achieve a good balance of properties. In general, larger boats, such as open canoes and C-2's require a more rigid formulation than kayaks and low-volume C-1's. Precise control of gel and cure times can be obtained by varying the amount of catalyst so that the time stays constant as the temperature varies. Temperatures of over 85 degrees F or under 60 degrees F require special precautions.

The following are the designations of some popular polyester systems used by homebuilders:

Company	Rigid Polyester	Flexible Polyester
USS Chemicals	MR 480 (Contains Wax) MR 12262 (Waxless)	MR 511(Waxless)
Reichold Chemicals	Polylite 33-067	Polylite 31-830
PPG Industries	Selectron 5238	Selectron 5238

John Sweet of Nittany Valley Boats, State College, PA. uses a 15% mixture of MR 511 with MR 12262 or MR 480. Ratios will vary substantially with the systems used; check with your seller before proceding.

The amount of CATALYST required is also quite variable, depending primarily on temperature but also on the promoters being used. Precision is not required except in hot weather, when little changes will make substantial differences.

The following is a table of the amount of catalyst needed to cure one gallon of polyester resin. Vinylesters require a bit more. Please note that this is DIFFERENT than previous editions of this MANUAL, since the industry standard for MEKP has been lowered from 11% to 9% active oxygen. As a result, it takes about 25% more MEKP to get the results to which you are accustomed.

WT/% MEKP	AMT cc's	AMT oz's	GEL TIME 60° F	GEL TIME 77°F	GEL TIME 90°F
.25	10	.32	190	70	45
.50	20	.64	75	31	20
.75	30	.96	65	20	12
1.0	40	1.26	25	13	8
2.0	80	2.52	13	6	2

USEFUL EQUIVILENTS: 1 Tsp = .17 oz.
1 Tablespoon = .5 oz.

VINYLESTER RESINS: Add approximately 25%

The following are John Sweet's recommendations for use with his polyester and vinylester resin systems sold through Nittany Valley Boats, State College, PA.

	Polyester Resin	Vinylester Resin
MINIMUM for slow cure; tick sections, high temperatures.	0.6 - 0.8 WT/% MEKP	0.8-1.0 WT/% MEKP
NORMAL for boat layups at moderate temperatures (65-75° F)	1.2-1.5 WT/% MEKP	1.7-2.0 WT/% MEKP
HOT BATCH for gel layers, small patches, low temperature use.	2.5-3.0 WT/% MEKP	3.4-4.0 WT/% MEKP

As you can see, these guidelines are a bit vague. Part of the difficulty is that MEKP loses potency when stored, so you can never tell exactly what you are getting unless you KNOW it's fresh. So.......

Here's what to do Mix up a small batch according to these guidelines. See how it performs relative to the table above, and modify your next batch accordingly. In summer, keep an eye on the thermometer. I have built on days when (with thunderstorms) the temperature varied over a 25° range!

CAUTION: The reduced percentage of oxygen in today's MEKP DOES NOT SIGNIFICANTLY REDUCE THE HAZZARDS associated with handling. ALWAYS USE SAFETY GOGGLES and protective clothing when handling or mixing MEKP.

OBTAINING THE CORRECT VINYLESTER:

Vinylesters as a class of resins have been available for quite some time, but it is only recently that they have become the material of choice for white water boatbuilders.

It has more strength and toughness than polyester, but without the complexity and side effects of epoxy. Despite obscure formulations and higher costs, use has spread to the commercial sector as well. The base resin is mixed with a second resin modified with VTBN (Vinyl-terminated-acrilonitrate butadiene) at about 25 PHR (Parts per hundred resin) to improve impact resistance. Like polyester, the system needs a promoter, and can be mixed with styrene or modified with thixotropes to obtain the exact characteristics desired. The exact formulation used by most whitewater boatbuilders is substantially thicker than polyester, though not as viscous as most epoxies.

RESIN: (Dow Chemical)	PROMOTER	CURING AGENT	USE
Derkane 470 Derkane 411 Derkane 510	Cobalt Napthenate .4 PHR Dimethylaniline .08 PHR	MEKP 1.0 PHR	Hand Layup
Derkane 8084 Derkane 8084 with 25 PHR Derkane 470	Cobalt napthenate .4 PHR (Dimethyaniline .08)	MEKP 1.0 PHR	Vacuum Bagging

Derkane 8084 is a pain to use in hand lay-up, and should never be used with tight weave cloths without a vacuum bag.

A heat cure is required if dimethylaniline is not used.

All vinylesters require a thixotrope despite their viscosity.

Most vinylesters are sold unpromoted, unwaxed, and unthixotroped to maximize shelf life (unlike most polyesters and epoxies). The hassles of gathering the proper chemicals and mixing them adds to their costs, and explains why some retailers charge so much !

BEWARE: VTBN-modified vinylester is an excellent adhesive and is capable of causing severe mold release problems ! Plenty of wax and careful application of PVA is essential.

PRO'S AND CON'S OF PIGMENTATION:

The natural color of cured resin is nominally clear, but in reality varies from a pale yellow to a dark brown. Because this lacks visual appeal, and because errors show up clearly in these laminates, most people prefer pigmented boats. Pigments are either opaque (solid colors) or transluscent (semi-transparent). The latter become opaque when used in greater quantities. The advantage of pigments is that they shield the resin from ultraviolet light, preventing degradation. This is very important for polyesters, which become quite brittle with age if not protected. The disadvantage is that some pigments must be added in great quantities to do the job. Many people have reported additional mold release problems and a weaker, more brittle laminate when using these pigments. My own advice is to use as little as possible, and this means buying high-quality translucent pigments which are compatable with the resin system you're using, and following manufacturer's guidelines carefully.

Here are the other procedures I can also recommend:

1. Mix up enough resin and pigment to allow you to make all pigmented parts of a given color. This means the first two layers of the deck and, if desired, the hull and the seat. This assures you of a good color match and avoids tedious, seldom-satisfactory color-matching attempts later. The inner layers of the boat will be laid up clear.

2. Lay the first layer up clear and allow to gel. Coat with two-part epoxy paint, and allow to dry. Then lay up the rest of the boat while the paint is still a bit tacky. This method is only suited to Epoxy resins, and allows the builder to paint complex designs onto the deck and hull which will not flake off.

3. There are a number of thin-pigmented outer layers available which, unlike thick, brittle premixed factory gel coats, are tough enough for white water boat use. Epoxy paint is one of these; Mad River Canoes uses another developed by Eastman Kodak. Most are laid in the mold and allowed to dry enough so that subsequent layers will not disturb it. More information in this area is needed by the author.

4. Lay up a polyester or nylon print cloth as the first layer. Bold prints and intricate designs produce the most striking effects. Choose an open-weave cloth. Avoid cotton; it is a resin sponge and adds very little strength. Fiberglass, surprisingly, will delaminate unless specially treated for plastics work. For predictable results, prepare a test patch first.

   Most fabrics are more tightly woven than conventional boat building materials, and are as a result more difficult to lay up. Allow plenty of time to work out entrapped air. The next layer should be pigmented <u>white</u> to show the cloth off to its best advantage. To test a <u>patch</u>, beat or flex it. Delamination should be confined to the area around the crack. Not recommended for use in the hull, or for people who enjoy pop-ups and enders. Another material to avoid are doubleknits; the two way stretch creates all sorts of problems.

5. Most home-built boats are made with one solid color or with the deck pigmented, the hull "natural". It used to be common to have a white hull and a colored deck to conceal scratches and abrasion, but styles change over the years and this is now unusual. A caution: Kevlar is <u>severely</u> effected by exposure to sunlight. It is considered very stylish to have clear boats with the natural color of the Kevlar showing through, but this will reduce the life of your boat. Smart builders will use pigments.

6. Heavy use of pigment will lengthen cure time. Compensate by adding a bit more MEKP to polyester and vinylester. Epoxies are less effected, and are best left alone.

BUYING PIGMENT: The best pigments for boatbuilders come dispersed in a medium which is compatable with your system. Dry pigments are difficult to handle and a real pain to mix. Don't try to mix two colors together; the results can be repulsive! Avoid opaque pigments; they give you a "washed out" appearance unless used in huge quantities. Translucent pigments give nice results in any concentration; the boat can be made opaque by adding the pigment to more than one layer. If you want to experiment, make a test patch first !

CLOTHS AND THEIR PROPERTIES:

The following is intended as a general guide to the fiber reinforcements most commonly used in building white water boats. Keep in mind that these materials are seldom used singley, and that the best laminates are made from combinations of two or more materials.

FIBERGLASS:

Also called E-Glass. Produced by many manufacturers. Comes in a variety of weights from 2-32+ oz/sq. yd.;10 Oz. Cloth is the recognised industry standard, however, and the most common component of white water boats.

CONFIGURATIONS: Flat Weave Cloth (Style 1800) wets out and squeegies easily. Fibers not twisted in weaving, so strength is maximized. This is the preferred material for hulls and decks.

Round Weave Cloth: (Style 7500): Conforms most easily to complex contours. Fabric is twisted in weaving for some loss of strength; absorbs slightly more resin than 1800. Recommended for coamings, outfitting, and complex decks.

Satin Weave Cloth: A very dense, tight weave. Stronger than 1800, but very difficult to work. Absorbs considerable resin. 5-24 oz/sq. yd. For vacuum bagging only.

Woven Roving:A Thick basket-weave material; quite quite heavy, fairly strong, inexpensive. Tends to delaminate easily. Used in making good molds and cheap, heavy boats.

Glass Mat: Randomized short fibers compressed into a felt-like cloth. Easy to work, cheap, heavy, and brittle. Absorbs lots of resin. Used to make molds, attach fittings, and as a filler for irregular cracks. Also used in making job-johnnies, bathtubs, etc. Not recommended for boats.

ADVANTAGES: Rigidity, good strength (particularly in compression) smooth wear, wide availability.

DISADVANTAGES: Brittle under impact; low performance in tension; dust and cloth is irritating to the skin; heavier because of density and resin absorption.

S-GLASS (Reichold Chemical)

Reichold is the only manufacturer of S-1014 Type S-Glass. A number of companies make the S-2 type, which is much less desirable. Most of the S-Glass available to boatbuilders is either a) S-2 material b) Seconds or overruns in a vide variety of weights and weaves, many of which absorb considerable resin c) a special weave for boatbuilders available through William Clark and Assoc. of Boulder, Colorado. (a flat weave similar to style 1800 E-Glass)

ADVANTAGES: Increases strength and rigidity (Style S-2 by 30%; Style S-1014 by 100%)compared to regular E-Glass.

DISADVANTAGES: Need to match resin with the finish; fabric is stiffer than E-Glass and harder to work with; incorrect weaves can lead to excessive resin absorption; high cost; poor availability.

NYLON (Burlington Industries)

A very tight-weave, lightweight fabric (Style 26115) is available from John R. Sweet of Nittany Valley Boats. Lighter weight, more open weave fabric (Style 16265) and heat-treated fabric for heat-cured systems (nylon shrinks) is available from Burlington Industries (500 yard minimum) in New York City. When boatbuilders speak of nylon, they mean 26115, a 4.2 Oz./ sq. yd. fabric, 66" wide.

ADVANTAGES: Good tear strength, impact strength, and elongation. Good in tension; light in weight; low in cost; absorbs very little resin.

DISADVANTAGES: Excessive flexibility; poor bonding with polyester resin; wrinkles if carelessly handled; fuzzes when abraded; low HDT. Wrinkles (if present) must be ironed out (low heat setting) prior to lamination.

CAP^{tm} POLYESTER (Noah Company)

A tight-weave, lightweight fabric similar to nylon. Material similar to this (Diolen) has been used extensively by European fabricators for quite some time; its development in the USA has been pioneered by Vladimir Vahana of Noah Corporation, Bryson City, NC. Weight: 7.5 oz/ sq. yd., Width 60"

ADVANTAGES: Good tear strength, impact strength, and elongation. Good in tension, light weight, low cost, wears smooth, absorbs little resin, bonds well to polyester resin.

DISADVANTAGES: Excessive flexibility; wrinkles easily if mishandled; low-to moderate HDT. Wrinkles must be ironed out prior to lamination.

POLYPROPYLENE (Vectra)

This material was used extensively in composites until the advent of nylon and CAP^{tm}. Weight 4.5 oz/sq. yd., Width 60"

ADVANTAGES: Excellent tear strength and good overall toughness. Light weight and high bulk makes it a superior "filler" in laminates.

DISADVANTAGES: <u>Very Poor</u> bonding to most resin systems; Excessive flexibility; low HDT; shrinks when heated, fuzzes when abraded. Floats on the surface of the resin, complicating layup. Wrinkles if carelessly handled.

DYNEL (Union Carbide)

Available as a 4.0 oz. Cloth. NOT RECOMMENDED for boatbuilding, but used instead for reinforcement in high wear areas.

ADVANTAGES: Very high abrasion resistance. Superior chemical resistance. Wears smooth.

DISADVANTAGES: Very low strength; very high resin absorption; used mostly as "wear layers" on C-1 paddle shafts.

KEVLAR 49 ARAMID^{tm} (DuPont; Fibers sold to numerous weavers)

CONFIGURATIONS: Many. Numerous weaves including open and satin. Also Kevlar Felt (mat) used for reinforcing the worn-out sterns of ABS canoes. For weaver Clark-Schwebel: Style 285 is recommended for vacuum-bagging; Style 500 for hand lay-up. Both are 5.0 oz cloths, available in 50" widths.

KEVLAR (Cont.)

ADVANTAGES: A low density material with outstanding rigidity and strength per unit of weight. Excellent in tension. Unexcelled as a component of tough, lightweight boats

DISADVANTAGES: High Cost; Fuzzes when abraded; dissapointing compressive strength; susceptability to ultraviolet degradation. All but the cost factor can be solved by using Kevlar in the inside layers only. Bonds poorly to polyester resins. Opaque color makes it difficult to spot and remove bubbles from the layup. Extremely difficult to cut; very sharp scissors must be used.

OTHER USEFUL MATERIALS:

FILLERS:

CAB-O-SIL: Actually powdered silica; a commonly used thixotropic agent. Makes resin cling to the inside of the mold, and can add considerable rigidity to the layup. Mix it with power tools; epoxies should be preheated before mixing. Resins containing cab-o-sil must be stirred before reach use, even in drum quantities, as the stuff tends to settle out. Also makes a paste similar to body putty when added to resin in large quantities. It is rock-hard, and very difficult to sand; don't use it ! And unless you are mixing your own system, or getting pinholes or patterning, stay away from cab-o-sil entirely.

SHORT FIBER ASBESTOS (Union Carbide Calidria Rg) An outstanding thixotrope which also possesses some reinforcing qualities. Since a little goes a long way, it alters resin properties much less than cab-o-sil. Would be the thixotrope of choice except that asbestos is carcinogenic. Dust from sanding layups in which Calidria Rg. has been used is also carcinogenic. Take all precautions when using or sanding this material to avoid inhalation.

MICROBALLOONS: Tiny hollow spheres of glass or plastic which can be added to Epoxy resin to form a strong, dense foam. Used for end pours (stern only, too fragile for the bow) and mixed with resin 1:1 or 2:1 by volume to thicken the laminate, adding stiffness without increasing weight. This technique is recommended for racing boats; the inevitable loss of strength makes it inadvisable for cruisers except in ratios of 4:1 or more. Substantially increases viscosity, making hand layup difficult and vacuum bagging a plus. Expert builders only.

CARBON FIBERS: An unusually stiff, brittle, costly material. Woven fabric costs of $75/yd makes use in kayaks impractical. Filament bundles and roving is used extensively for reinforcement of lightweight racing boats; cost is under $1 per yard, and a little goes a long way. Can also be used by builders to stiffen key areas of cruising boats to minimize fatigue.

SAWDUST, ETHAFOAM SCRAPS, and CHOPPED FIBERGLASS SCRAPS are also used as fillers in bow and stern plugs. Results in a dense plug similar to milled fiber castings. One builder mixes his plugs putty thick and spoons it in place.

FLOUR: One of the real problems with fillers is they are difficult to purchase in small amounts. Bill McKnight uses all-purpose flour as a thixotrope for making putties and thickening small quantities of resin. It's non-toxic and readily available. CAUTION: do not use self-rising or other adulterated products.

MOLD RELEASE AGENTS:

WAX: Used to polish the mold, forming a barrier between it and the resin. Many specialized waxes are available (most builders prefer CERA waxes), but any good quality wax (Johnson's, Butcher's, and other paste waxes) with a high carnuba content will do the job. BEWARE of liquid waxes, clean & shine products, and anything containing silicones; these will leach through the PVA and cause the boat to stick. When working with resins with known release problems, it will probably be smarter to stick with industrial formulations. Ask your supplier or mold renter for recommendations.

PVA (Polyvinyl Alcohol): A thin, green or blue liquid which dries to form a thin, water soluble barrier between the wax and the resin, further protecting the mold. Apply carefully and evenly with a clean rag, a clean, fine brush, or spray-up apparatus. Must be washed off the boat after "popping" it from the mold. Also available as <u>sheets</u> for patching and vacuum-bagging applications. You will need a thickness of 2-4 mils for vacuum bagging.

WAX PAPER is often used as a non-stick surface on a workbench when laying up small parts or to cover patches. Resin does not adhere to it; sometimes it does not peel off all easily afterwards. More durable than plastic supermarket wraps.

PLASTIC WRAPS: Used as a non-stick working surface or covering. Not all wraps work! Polyester, vinylester, and epoxy do not stick to polyethylene (PE). They DO stick to PVC (Surprisingly). I use Handi-wrap myself, but you can determine the composition of any plastic wrap by reading the label.

FOAMS:

Most foam is difficult to purchase in small quantities except from retailers. Then it is expensive. Several mail order operations (NOC, Wildwater Designs) sell sheets of Ethafoam; Minicell and PVC are often sold as sleeping pads. All are closed-cell foams which do not absorb water.

ETHAFOAM is a semi-rigid polyethylene foam used extensively by the packaging industry. It is rigid enough for bulkheads and walls, yet flexible enough for padding. Used extensively in outfitting white water boats. The best way to buy it is in 2"x 2'x9' sheets from a foam or packaging supplies house. Mail order houses sell "quarter sheets" cut down to mailable size. Problem: being a "semi-closed cell foam" it will absorb water and get heavy with age.

STYROFOAM is lighter, stiffer, cheaper, and more brittle than Ethafoam. As a result, it leads to the formation of "stress risers" and wears poorly. Used when weight, not strength, is of paramount importance. The "Expanded Styrene" sold at building supply houses is tougher than the marine version and more readily available. The cheaper polystyrene "bead foam" crumbles at the slightest touch and makes a mess. CAUTION: Use Epoxy resin as glue; contact cement(and polyester <u>and</u> vinylester resins) will dissolve the foam.

MINICEL is a trade name for crosslinked polyethylene, which is used extensively as life vest flotation. It's a lot like Ethafoam, but lighter and (unfortunately) less available. Makes superior walls, padding, and outfitting.

PVC FOAM, alias Ensolite^{tm}, is a soft closed cell foam used for life vest flotation (Extrasport Life Vests). Half-inch and lesser thicknesses are great for padding.

NEOPRENE is wet suit material, generally sold with a nylon backing for wetsuit and sprayskirt fabrication. Cheaper "sharkskins" and other lesser grades are slightly stiffer than the prime stuff, but make no difference when used as padding. Soft and expensive. Makes great padding, esp. if you can get an old wetsuit to cut up!

GLUES:

CONTACT CEMENT and WET SUIT GLUE are similar chemically and in practice. They harden as a flammable solvent (benzene or toluene) evaporates. CAUTION: USE IN A WELL-VENTED AREA. PUT OUT ALL FLAMES. DO NOT SMOKE ! Both sides to be joined should be coated, allowed to dry tack-free (sticky, but will not pull away when touched), lined up carefully (the stuff really grabs; you get only one chance) and pressed together. The Feds, out of concern with our safety, are pushing a new "safe" glue which, unfortunately, is water soluble!!! If you can't find the old kind (it is amber, not white) get some BARGE CEMENT from your local shoemaker or his supplier (great stuff),or use wet suit glue. DO NOT INHALE THE FUMES; they'll eat your liver

HOT GLUES, sold by Sears and other places, are great for gluing ethafoam to itself, repairing river chasers, etc. Definitely the class way to go: no fumes, much neater. The "catch" is that you have to buy a special heated "glue gun" to apply the glues, which ups the cost quite a bit.

MOST RESINS make excellent glues, and can be used for most gluing chores. Epoxy and vinylester are much better than polyesters. Do not use polyester on styrofoam; it will dissolve it and leave you with nothing.

DESCRIPTION OF LAYUPS:

The materials used and the order in which they are laid down comprise the "layup". As we mentioned before, an effort should be made to find complementary materials, and to lay them up in sufficient quantities for your intended use. In general, a deck has fewer layers than a hull. A 5/4 (five layer hull, four layer deck) is a heavyweight cruiser; a 3/2 is a lightweight racer; a 4/3 is a good compromise. This does not take into account reinforcing. The weight of the cloths used and the amount of resin consumed determine the final weight of the boat. The lighter boats are inclined to be too flexible unless materials are chosen with care; big boats, such as C-2's and downriver designs, must be laid up stiffer than slalom kayaks and small volume slalom C-1's. If WALLS are indicated, this means that the boat is too flexible to be used safely without internal deck support. ALL 3/2 layups need ribs or walls regardless !

Weight varies with the design & materials used, the amount of reinforcement, and the skill of the builder. Here are some approximate figures:

LAYUP:	5/4	4/3	3/2	KEVLAR
Kayaks	35	30	25	18
C-1's	45	35	30	25
C-2's	60	45	35	30

Subtract 10% for low-volume designs, or if you are an experienced builder. Add 20% for wildwater boats. The C-2 figures are good for a 15' open canoe; add 10% for 17'; 15% for 18'6.

HOW LAMINATES WORK:

As we have mentioned before, white water laminates are underdesigned for the stresses they must bear. The only way that they can survive is to be flexible enough to bend away from an impact, absorbing most of the stress. The craft must also be stiff enough to hold its shape for performance and safety. Some of these characteristics are determined by the resin system used, but we are making the assumption that you have located a suitable one. Since a 25% increase in thickness doubles the stiffness of a layup, quantities of material have a substantial effect on its characteristics. Given a standard four layer hull and similar resin systems, the cloth types used as reinforcing fibers and the order in which they are laid down will have the greatest effect on final performance.

Initially, whitewater boats were constructed entirely of fiberglass. These were stiff enough, but brittle. As a result, most were heavily reinforced and ended up impossibly heavy. The first great advance was when someone added a layer of polypropylene. Although it is far too flexible to use alone (yes, Virginia, they tried that too!) it stretched where fiberglass would break and held the boat together! Since then, almost all white water boats have been made from composites: a combination of two or more reinforcing fibers. This substantial improvement is born out by Chip Queitzsch's test results. (see E/E/N/E)

In a laminate under flexure, the strain is born by the outer and innermost layers of the laminate. The intervening layers increase rigidity by adding thickness and take up interlaminar shear stress, and are put in tension and compression only if the outsides of the "sandwich" is damaged. When a stretchy, low-modulus material (such as nylon) is used on the outside, the material is easy to bend but hard to break. A high modulus material on the outsides (such as fiberglass) is stiffer, but more brittle. The biggest problem with the inside material is delamination as a result of shear stress. If there is any problem with the resin adhering to the inner cloth, damage will result.

Lets look at some practical examples:

N = Nylon; E=Fiberglass; P=Polypropylene

Layup 1: N/E/E/N (Penn State Layup)
Layup 2: E/P/P/E (Philadelphia Layup)

The G/P/P/G layup was originally developed by the Philadelphia Canoe club to build racing boats. The result is a stiff hull, samples of which perform well in engineering tests (Chip Queitzsch tested N/E/E/N, a very close relative). The problem is that Polypropylene (and, to a lesser extent, Nylon) have <u>severe</u> bonding problems with most resins, <u>particularly</u> polyester. The core delaminates under stress, and thus these boats do not stand up well to rough handling.

The N E/E/N layup, pioneered by the Penn State Outing Club, did poorly in Chip's testing, but better in real life. Its tough outer layer, while making the laminate flexible, was very difficult to puncture or tear. Second, the fiberglass core bonds well to almost all resins, minimizing delamination. Lastly, although the internal core of fiberglass will crack under impact, the nylon will remain whole and minimize the spread of damage. There is a substantial amount of damage done (shown by Chip's testing) which is not visible to the eye. But damaged or not, a lot of these boats did very well on the river.

Chip's research suggests an alternative layup: E/N/E/N. Having fiberglass on the outer layer improves stiffness; nylon on the inner layer makes for superior toughness. Each material is used where its strengths do the most good: nylon in tension; fiberglass in compression. The results show this to be true. The only problem is that an exposed glass layer develops short, sharp fibers which stick out in a worn hull. Handling such a boat is uncomfortable, and gives some folks a severe skin rash. As a result, some bulders cover E-Glass or S-Glass with a very thin, light, polyester or nylon "veil" (1 oz/sq. yd). Great stuff if you can get it !

Beyond this, improved performance requires stiffer, higher modulus, lighter weight materials. Racing weight craft, which are often extremely flexible because their laminates are so thin, are particularly in need of this assistance. Most of the attention in the last five years has focused on Kevlar, a material which is as stiff as fiberglass, but lighter and tougher. It is a high-modulus synthetic, seemingly combining the advantages of fiberglass and nylon. In practice, however, this is not the case. All-Kevlar layups are overly flexible (though improved over an all-nylon layup) and while light weight, they are disapointing in compression and literally flex themselves to death. The addition of a single layer of fiberglass to the outside of the laminate (E/K/K/K) greatly improves stiffness and compression, and has become the preferred racing layup. Kevlar, though expensive, cuts the weight of each layer by 30% over fiberglass. For the hard-core racer, this feature alone (as opposed to improved toughness) would be enough to interest them.

For "cruising weight" boats with superior performance characteristics, the idea is to lay the fiberglass on the outside, where its compressive strength will do the most good, and the Kevlar on the inside, where its superior strength in tension will be put to use. About ten years ago a higher modulus glass fiber cllled S-Glass was developed which is much less brittle and tougher than regular E-Glass. After trying all S-Glass boats (too brittle), some builders started replacing E-Glass with S-Glass in composite layups. The "S/S/K/K" and "S/K/S/K" laminations were proven to be the toughest combinations, but cost was high. E/E/K/K and E/E/N/K were used in an effort to cut custs. "N/G/G/K" is an "improved version" of the Penn State layup; John Sweet recommends N/G/G/K/K as an "Expedition weight" boat.

When planning a laminate, keep in mind the characteristics of the resin you are using. Synthetic cores delaminate easily when used with polyester resin, so that if durability is important to you, avoid using them except on the outer and inner layers. A possible exception is Noah's CAP polyester, which not only bonds better, but wears smoother when used on the outside of the hull. Information supplied by Noah suggests that CAP substituted for nylon in the "Penn State" and "Philadelphia" layup would improve both, with the former being flexible and puncture resistant; the latter being stiffer and less prone to delamination. For maximum stiffness, Noah recommends G/G/CAP/CAP. Noah uses G/CAP/K/CAP in their cruising weight boats. If you are using high-performance reinforcements, don't skimp on the resin. Use vinylester or epoxy for best results.

RECOMMENDATIONS:

For those who are now more confused than when they started. There are many variables, so it would be best to check with the person you buy your resin from for confirmation.

Polyester/Conventional materials: G/CAP/G/CAP
G/CAP/CAP/G

With Polyester or Epoxy resins:	Racing:	G/K/K (Three layer hull)
	Cruising:	S/S/K/K (Ultimate Construction)
		S/K/S/K " "
		G/G/K/K (Compromise construction)
		G/CAP/G/CAP (low-cost option)
		G/CAP/CAP/G " " "
		N/S/S/K/K (Ultimate Expedition)
		N/G/G/K/K (Compromise expedition)
		CAP/G/G/K/K (Low-cost option)

NOTES ON CORE MATERIALS:

Interlaminar cores are used to increase rigidity by adding thickness. These materials add little weight, but also increase interlaminar shear stress. Since cores are substantially weaker than the other materials used in the laminate, canoes and kayaks using them are less durable than those built with conventional layups. They are used extensively in the construction of marathon and flatwater cruising canoes, where durability is not an issue. You will also see them less commonly used in whitewater racing craft, particularly in the larger wildwater boats and especially in C-2's.

The following core materials are in common use:

AIREX FOAM: The old standby; 4-6 lbs/ft^3 closed cell PVC. Easily heat formed· not brittle or stiff. Minimum thickness 1/4". Heavier density improves strength, increases weight, and produces no additional rigidity.

KLEGECEL: 4-6 lb/ft^3. More brittle, but stiffer, with greater compressive strength than Airex. Brittleness makes handling difficult, and this offsets its improved structural qualities.

HONEYCOMB: Hexcel HEH-10, phenolic impregnated kraft paper. 3-5 lb/ft^3, less strength and weight than foams. Comes in regular OX for compound contours or FLEXCRE for extreme contours. Get the smalles possible cell size (1/8") for minimum patterning.

BALSA: Maximum strength for its weight. Can absorb considerable water if improperly treated, or if ends not sealed. Best for large structures which never break.

SYNTACTICS: A very dense foam created by mixing resin with microspheres, phenolic microbaloons, styrofoam beads, or epoxy beads. Can be mixed on site, or bought as board stock. about 35 lb/ft^3 with good shear strength. Inclined to be brittle. Must be sprayed up with special guns, as ordinary spray tools break bubbles. Hyperform made excellent racing boats with this material.

COREMAT: Polyester fibers and microbaloons made into a material which looks like a paper towel. Recommended by John Scriner, New Wave Kayaks. Many thicknesses, 1 ml thickness recommended for kayaks, 2 ml for open canoes. This is the only material which can be hand-laminated by the average home builder. Cost .20-.30 sq/ft (in '86) in 540 sq/ft rolls from West Point Pepperill, P.O. Box 71, West Point, GA 31833 PH: 706-645-4000. DO NOT HEAT CURE.

FABRICATION TECHNIQUES: All cores are interlaminar materials. Use between the layers of your craft, not on the outside or inside. Use a 1-2 layer skin. Coremat laminates like cloth. Honeycomb and Foam can be worked into shape with a heat gun; pierce at 1" intervals to permit resin and air to escape. Except for coremat, vacuum-bagging is almost a necessity. Apply vacuum until resin is cured, then add the inside layers of the laminate.

RIBS AND KEELS can be constructed of foam covered with cloth. Thicker ribs are stiffer; 3/8"-1/2" normally used. Trapezoidal shape minimizes formation of stress risers. Can be bagged in with layup or put in afterwards. Cover foam with fiberglass (1-2 layers) or Kevlar. Steve rock says: use 1 layer or unidirectional Kevlar if you want to stand on the deck; two layers if you want to bounce, with an outer layer of regular fiberglass.

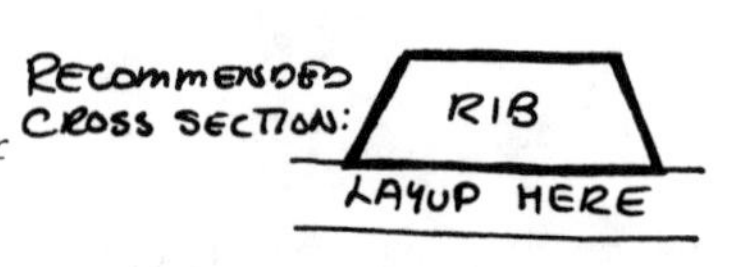

QUANTITIES NEEDED FOR BOATBUILDING:

Exact resin consumption figures vary with the size of the boat being built. The "minimum" is a bare minimum for low-volume boats; the "maximum" is probably a bare minimum for wildwater boats. Unless you have ready access to materials, always over-buy so you won't be caught short ! Cloth consumption figures assume 1 boat layer per width, with the extra being used for reinforcements. With wider fabrics, it may be possible to get two layers out, particularly for kayaks. Check the width of your pattern and the cutting chart before ordering.

ITEM	KAYAKS	C-1's	C-2's
Resin	2.0-3.0 Gals	2.5-3.5 Gals	3.0-4.0 Gals
Cloth	4.5 yds/layer	5.0 yds/layer	5.5 yds/layer
	31 yds	35 yds	38.5 yds.
(add .5 yds/layer for wildwater boats)			
Ethafoam	7'x1'x2"	10'x1'x2"	12'x1'x2"
(for walls only. Wildwater C-boats require more than 12" width)			

1 gallon of most resins = 8.5 lbs. or 4 kilograms (approx); Will vary with the precise system being used. Most systems are sold by weight, rather than by volume.

When ordering, allow plenty of delivery time, particularly when dealing with distant wholesale sources. Buying from a local dealer or club is often worthwhile. I'd pay extra cost for reliable delivery. Before ordering ethafoam, read the section on outfitting so you'll be sure to get enough.

SHOP EQUIPMENT INVENTORY:

NB: Vacuum bagging requires additional tools, which will be listed separately. You'll still need the following:

ELECTRIC DRILL, 3/8", variable speed, with the following attachments:

DISC SANDER: Boat Technology sells THE BEST I have seen. Will outlast anything else; worth the price.

MIXER: With 12" shaft. You'll want to stick it through an old garbage can lid or equivalent so as not to splatter you or your tool when mixing.

DRILL BITS: 3/8" is handy for grab loop holes.

If you are planning to do a lot of sanding (as you will if you are constructing a plug for a mold) get a power disc sander. Continuous use will burn out an electric drill. Clean the openings periodically to prevent dust buildup.

HACKSAW with several blades, or a sabre saw. 24 teeth/inch is a good size.

HOOKED LINOLEUM KNIFE, UTILITY KNIFE or somesuch for trimming. Must be stiff enough for good control; exacto knives are sharp, but too flimsy, as are most replaceable-blade knives. Get a sharpening stone and learn to keep your blade razor-sharp !

SHEET METAL SHEARS, very heavy duty, can also be used for trimming. END SNIPS are also helpful. Both are optional.

SCISSORS, top quality, sharp, large, for cutting cloth. Your best pair must be reserved for cutting synthetics (nylon, Kevlar) and never used on fiberglass. Fiberglass shears are hard to keep sharp, so don't waste them cutting gunky cloth. An el cheapo pair will suffice for "wet work".

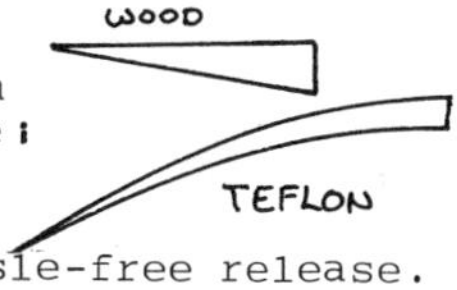

PLASTIC OR WOODEN WEDGES, gradually tapered as shown, do a good job of popping a boat from the mold without undue violence. Teflon is the material of choice, available from Clark and Assoc. or J.R. Sweet. Thin taper and super flexibility gets you under the boat for a hassle-free release.

A SURFORM FILE or WOOD RASP for smoothing and shaping molded parts such as cockpit rims, fittings, etc. Reinforced plastics are very hard on all edged tools, so keep replaceable blades handy. An AUTO BODY FILE, which can be contoured to the work at hand, is expensive, but ideal for extensive work.

OLD SCREWDRIVER or BAYONET for prying mold flanges apart, chipping resin globs off the floor, and other choice tasks.

EXTENSION CORD to give mobility to power tools. Wax the cord beforehand so that resin spills won't glue it to the floor. A TROUBLE LIGHT at the end of a cord is handy for working inside the boat.

A BIG FIRE EXTINGUISHER, just in case. The small ones don't do much good. Often you can borrow one from a school or institution for short periods. But you should have one in the house somewhere, anyway.

PAINT ROLLERS for applying resin to the mold. Ideal for big jobs, like wildwater C-2 hulls; not useful in tight places. Don't try to clean; have plenty of disposables on hand. Not essential, but occasionally useful

HEAT LAMPS for prewarming resin or maintaining a heat cure. Use infra-red lamps; ultra violet (sunlamps) are more expensive, and may damage the layup. CAUTION: Watch temp. carefully!

CLEAN, SOFT RAG for applying PVA. Should not be used for anything else. A spray-bottle also works well; a compressed-air sprayer is, of course, ideal.

ONE RESPIRATOR PER WORKER for protection against dust and fumes. These are discussed at length in the safety section; suffice it to say that everyone should use one when building !!

DISPOSABLES:

3+ PAIRS OF GLOVES to protect your hands from the resin (fewer are needed for vaccum bagging) Boat Technology sells the best kind; playtex gloves are durable, but clumbsy; surgical gloves fit well, but gradually dissolve in resin. Always wear gloves for "wet work"; ie: work involving resin.

DISPOSABLE CLOTHING is a must. Resin-contaminated clothing is ruined, and should not be worn, as it can cause skin irritation. Boat Technology sells an inexpensive coverall. You can also make a good shirt by cutting head and arm holes in a large trash bag. Use a waste-basket sized plastic bags or a bathing cap to protect your hair when working inside the boat.

TRASH BAGS are also needed to line the inside of various containers used to control the spread of the gooey mess. The more trash cans, the neater your shop will be.

BARRIER CREAM, such as Ply #9, Kerodex (the latter is available in most drug stores) acts as a resin barrier on exposed skin parts, such as the collar and cuff area. Used on hands, it makes cleanup easier. Should not be used in place of gloves ! It cannot be relied on to that extent.

HANDI-WRAP or WAX PAPER: used to create a working surface to which cured resin won't stick. If you are vacuum-bagging, PVA-film which has been "worn-out" also serves the same function.

GALLON MILK JUGS for storing resin and, cut down, as a mixing pot. A dozen will be more than enough for a boat, so start saving !!

PAPER TOWELS: Many uses.

TONGUE DEPRESSORS: For mixing resin. They're always clean, and cheap, which is more than I can say for other things I have used. A few dozen will suffice.

GRADUATED JUGS for mixing by volume. A syringe (without needle) or a teaspoon/tablespoon baking setup also works well. You can make your own graduated jugs using paper cups, a ruler, and an accurate scale to determine the graduations. CAUTION: in some cases measurement by weight is not the same thing as measurement by volume because of density differences. If you need a scale, you'll need one which is accurate to the nearest tenth of a gram.

TERRYCLOTH (BATH) TOWELS: For applying wax to the mold, and for buffing and polishing that wax. Must be kept clean, as dirt and dust will scratch the mold.

PLASTIC DROP CLOTHS to cover the floors. Newspaper does not work as well: resin can seep through it, bonding it to the floor. A thick coating of newsprint works in a pinch.

SANDPAPER: medium grit in discs for finish work; coarse discs for roughing; 200-600 grit wet sandpaper in sheets for mold repair; polishing. No power tools in the mold, please!

MASKING TAPE for keeping resin from getting where it doesn't belong. I sometimes use fiberglass strapping tape in preference to masking tape, since it holds together better and is easier to remove.

AUTO BODY APPLICATORS (Squeegies) or PAINTBRUSHES (1"&2" are the usual tools for applying resin to a mold. I use squeegies in open areas, a brush in bows, sterns, and other tight places. Lay in extra brushes or the appropriate solvent for cleaning.

BOATHOLDERS FOR BOATBUILDERS

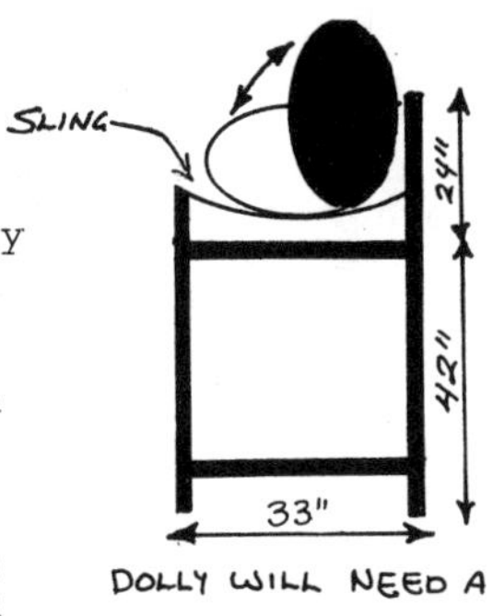

BOAT DOLLY: Will hold the boat steady at a convenient height either horizontally or vertically. Use shock cord to hold in place. For delicate work, slings can be used. (molds should be stored in slings when not in use) Two boards 8' long which go between the two dollies will support a wood-framed mold.

ROPE BOAT HANGERS allow a boat or mold to be suspended from the ceiling when not in use at any given height. This allows you to keep the boat out of the way, yet allows quick worker access. The boat is most easily worked on if you can brace it against the wall as you go.

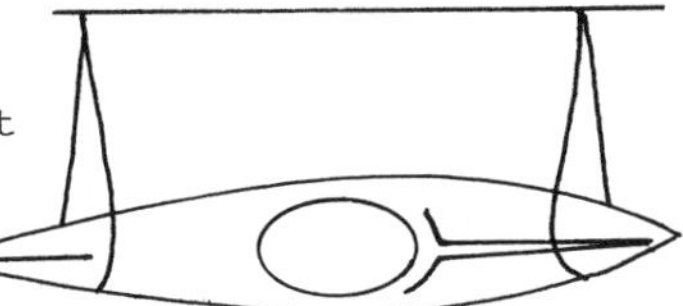

SETTING UP SHOP:

WHERE TO WORK: Most people prefer to work indoors, where the environment can be controlled and dust kept to a minimum. For most of these people, the biggest problem is to do this without contaminating their living quarters. Any time you work in a building, the fumes and dust take over everything, making the rest of the place unpalatable if not unhealthy. A free-standing garage is, for these reasons, ideal. Many clubs rent their own shop in an industrial area, or use school facilities.

HEATING AND VENTILATION are major worries. Most boatbuilding is done in winter, so a temperature in between 65 and 70 degrees must be maintained. Since everything associated with boatbuilding is highly flammable, an open flame heater of any kind is out. Ventilation works at cross-purposes with heating except in summer. In enclosed spaces, cross-ventilation must be maintained, or the workers must breathe air from the outside thru masks for safety. If only one fan is available, place it low in the shop, facing out (fumes sink). In very humid climates, a dehumidifier/air conditioner system may be needed on the hottest, muggiest days for quality control. It is usually better not to build in high humidity or in temperatures over 85 degrees.

THE GREAT OUTDOORS is an ideal shop. Ventilation is excellent, and summer heat all too reliable. A porch or an old barn is ideal for the purpose, since you are protected from rain and direct sunlight (and, to a lesser extent, insects, dust, and low-flying birds).

> CAUTIONS: Be <u>careful</u> about allowing a boat to cure in the sun. It works great with some systems, but with others (polyester) distortion and bubbling will result. NEVER lay up in the sun, as it will shorten gel time incredibly.
>
> AVOID WATER, as it will cause an uncured laminate to "blush" (turn white) and degrade its strength substantially. A <u>heavy</u> <u>dew</u> is too much!

A SAMPLE LAYOUT for a small club shop is shown on the next page. Remember that fiberglass work will bring out the slob in anyone, and that anything you don't want damaged is best left out of the way. Ample trash containers appropriately placed also help a lot.

SAMPLE SHOP LAYOUT:

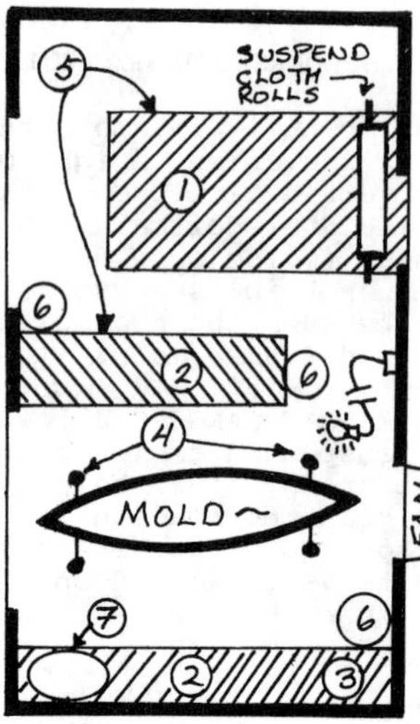

1) Your cutting table needs to be at least 4'x14' and probably 6'x17' for a high-volume club shop in which wildwater boats will be made. Keep it out of the way so sticky messes will not be left there.
2) Counters are needed on both sides of the layup area. Cover with plastic prior to use.
3) The scale should be placed outside the normal traffic pattern.
4) Boat dollies are needed to hold the mold.
5) All materials and tools should be kept out-of-the-way when not in use.
6) Trash cans should be placed all around the work area (otherwise, the trash ends up on the floor.)
7) Provide a place to wash-up in an out-of-the-way place. Under no circumstances should "unclean" people invade your living quarters ! For best results, have a complete change of clothes and shoes inside the shop.
8) It goes without saying that boat shops are no place for young children. Many of the chemicals are DEADLY POISON. For this reason, it's smart to lock the shop when its not in use. Child-proofing is NOT an option.

SAFETY CONSIDERATIONS:

Boatbuilding Health and Safety by Gary E. Myers

Gary is an expert in industrial hygiene; the recognition, evaluation, and control of occupational health hazzards. He is on the editorial committee of the American Industrial Hygiene Assn., and is currently employed in this field for a large research facility. This is one of many of his publications.

Like many high-technology activities, boatbuilding presents a number of serious health and safety hazard . to the unwary. Health impairment and/or injuries can be either acute or chronic. An acute effect is one whose symptoms appear immediately after the insult or shortly thereafter, and whose effects are temporary; a chronic effect is one whose symptoms appear at any time after the insult (usually not immediately) and are, for all practical purposes, permanent. A smashed knuckle, for example, is an acute injury, but the stiffness which persists for years afterwards is chronic. Boatbuilding materials, if used carelessly, can produce either type of injury.

EPOXY SYSTEMS vary in their hazard potential, but all are dangerous in the uncured state. Acute effects of overexposure depend upon the route of exposure.

1) SKIN CONTACT is the most common route, and contact dermatitis often results. In its mild form, symptoms include redness, itching, and swelling; in more cases, blisters, oozing, and intolerable itching are followed by crusting and scaling of the skin. Severity depends on the individual but often progresses after contact has ceased. Don't think that you needn't be careful until you notice a rash! In addition, amine hardeners are capable of producing severe chemical burns. Polyamides are considered to be only mildly irritating in the acute sense, but when mixed with epoxy the combination can produce severe dermatitis.

2) RESPIRATORY irrtation results from excessive inhalation of epoxy system vapors. The epoxies themselves do not pose much problem at room temperature, but curing agents and reactive diluents are much more volatile. The effects range from a mild, tickling cough to more serious irritation, or an asthma-like attack. Since it normally takes several days (ed. note: or weeks) for an epoxy system to cure completely, sanding or grinding a fresh layup can produce an aerosol of irritating particles. High-speed grinding of even old layups can decompose cured epoxy into toxic gasses.

CHRONIC EFFECTS can be summed up in one word:sensitization. A sensitized individual has been made allergic to epoxy systems (ed. note: in much the same way a non-allergic individual becomes sensitized to poison ivy). Subsequent exposures, however slight, will cause oozing,blistering dermatitis possibly accompanied by respiratory distress. This is a permanent condition caused by repeated overexposure to epoxy. How many times is "repeated?" You may as well ask how many angels can dance on the head of a pin: the answer is;from one to many, depending on your individual body chemistry. There's really only one way to find out, and that's the hard way..... and once you've found out, you can never work with epoxies again.

EPOXY SYSTEM components vary in toxicity. The pure resins are in general less hazardous than the other components, but they are not inert. DGEBA will cause contact dermatitis, and has been documented as a sensitizer. CURING AGENTS produce the greatest danger because of their volatility as well as their potency. BGE is the most common diluent. Being both a potent sensitizer and fairly volatile, it can act via either the skin or respiratory tract. AMINE HARDENERS are just plain awful: they are caustic and produce severe chemical burns to the skin or eyes; their vapors are extremely irritating to both the eyes and the respiratory tract; they will cause contact dermatitis; they have caused liver disease and testicular degeneration in experimental animals.POLYAMIDES when combined with epoxies, have a significant sensitizing potential. These are only a few examples. TREAT ALL COMPONENTS OF EPOXY SYSTEMS WITH THE GREATEST OF RESPECT !!

PERSONS WITH PRE-EXISTING CONDITIONS such as allergies, skin disease, asthma, or other respiratory problems should not work with epoxies without consulting their physicians first. EVERYONE ELSE MUST TAKE ALL PRECAUTIONS TO MINIMIZE CONTACT.

POLYESTER SYSTEMS (Ed note: and vinylesters) present somewhat different hazards from those of epoxies. They are normally considered "safer" than epoxies, but this is only true in some respects.

ACUTE EFFECTS again depend on the route of exposure

1) Skin hazards are similar to epoxies, except that the dermatitis is usually (but not always) less severe. DIMETHYLANILINE, an accelerator, is a central nervous system depressant which can be absorbed through the skin. STYRENE and MEKP can cause dermatitis, and MEKP can also cause chemical burns. (Ed. Note: and very severe eye burns !)

2) RESPIRATORY HAZARDS from polyesters are actually <u>greater</u> than with most epoxies, since system components are generally more volatile. Headache, drowsiness, dizziness, loss of appetite, nausea, sneezing, and coughing are common symtoms. Prolonged overexposure can cause serious injury. Hyperemia and gross hemorrages of the lungs are common in experimental animals exposed to MEKP vapor.

3) EYE HAZARDS are similar to those from epoxies. MEKP is very irritating, and can cause severe injury. Other components are equally capable of doing damage.

CHRONIC EFFECTS of overexposure to polyester systems include: SKIN SENSITIZATION (rare, but documented); LIVER DAMAGE, including blood and protein irregularities from skin absorption of dimethylaniline. LIVER AND KIDNEY DAMAGE from inhalation of MEKP has been found in experimental animals.

FLAMMABILITY of polyester system components is a serious hazard. STYRENE is quite flammable, and <u>explosive</u> concentrations of vapor can accumulate. MEKP is basically unstable, and although sold diluted, it is still flammable and its vapors are explosive. DIRECT CONTACT OF PEROXIDE CATALYSTS AND CONCENTRATED PROMOTERS OR ACCELERATORS MUST BE PREVENTED AT ALL TIMES, OR FIRE AND/OR EXPLOSION MAY RESULT.

FIBERGLASS is not toxic, but is rather quite irritating to the skin and respiratory tract. ACUTE EFFECTS include dermatitis from skin contact, and coughing and sneezing from inhalation. CHRONIC EFFECTS are not well documented; at one time it was thought that there were none, but chronic lung disease resulting from excessive inhalation of ultrafine glass fibers has been reported. (Ed. note: Caution should be exercised when sanding)(Ed. note: Drs. inform me this is <u>not</u> technically silicosis)

PREVENTION OF DISEASE AND INJURY in an industrial sense is often beyond the means of the homebuilder. Anyone planning to open a shop should become thoroughly familiar with OSHA requirements. In many instances, though, simple precautions are quite effective. Control is the first line of defense against injury, and serious, disciplined efforts along this line must always be made.

VENTILATION is the first line of defense when work is performed indoors. One of the most effective schemes is, happily, easy to set up. Position the mold near a window, place an exhaust fan in the window, and open windows on the opposite side of the room. This way, the fan will draw fresh air across the room, sweeping vapors away and out the window before they build up to high concentrations. You should shoot for six room air changes per hour, so the fan must have 100 cubic feet per minute of rated capacity for each 1000 cubic feet of room volume. A one-car garage 15x20x8 (2400 cubic feet) needs a fan with a <u>minimum</u> capacity of 240 cfm. If your work cannot be positioned near a window (or, ed. note, if you have only one window), double these figures. Be sure to build a baffle around the exhaust fan which blocks off all excess area of the window for most efficient operation; otherwise, the fan will not move air at its rated capacity. If you are concerned about airborn dust, tape furnace filters over the window.

CAUTION: DO NOT TRY OTHER SYSTEMS UNLESS YOU HAVE EXPERT ADVICE. The entire subject is highly technical, and a poorly designed hood or other system could be a danger in itself by inspiring false confidence.

HOUSEKEEPING is a control measure which is often overlooked. Merely keeping your shop orderly during a project increases your safety,as well as your craftsmanship and sense of humor. (You won't try to "make do" with the wrong tool if the right one is in its proper place, tripping hazzards will be minimized, and potential for spills reduced, etc.) CLEAN UP ALL SPILLS IMMEDIATELY to minimize fire hazard and to keep hazardous materials from being tracked around where kids or pets can get into them.

PERSONAL HYGIENE goes hand-in-hand with housekeeping. If you spill something on yourself, wash it off at once. Dermatitis and sensitization result from the LENGTH OF CONTACT as well as the FREQUENCY. Both epoxies and polyesters can be removed effectively by a number of waterless hand cleaners. Do not use those containing gritty abrasives, as these can scratch the skin and leave it susceptible to dermatitis. Sugar Beet Products SBS-33 is a particularly good, non-abrasive cleaner. Follow this with a thorough washing in mild soap and water. Soap and water is also the best way to remove tiny, irritating fiber-glass particles from the skin. Lather gently, as vigorous rubbing will imbed the particles more deeply. Clothing should be laundered frequently to prevent buildup of glass and resin. (Ed note: make use of disposables whenever possible.)

NOTE: These precautions are good for everyone you associate with, as they help control the spread of toxic and irritating materials into your home.

SOLVENTS come to mind whenever cleanup is mentioned. The ones we are talking about dissolve tough plastics, and have very nasty side effects. All organic solvents have some effect on the central nervous system and the skin. The best advice for using solvents as cleaning agents is: don't, unless you absolutely have to-- and then, only with extreme caution. ACETONE (the solvent for polyester) is of low acute toxicity and has no chronic affects, but is <u>extremely and violently flammable</u> and its vapors are <u>explosive</u>. METHLY ISOBUTYL KETONE (MIBK, the solvent for epoxy) is extremely irritating to the eyes and respiratory tract; headache, dizziness and nausea may result. GASOLINE is a motor fuel, so leave it in the tank where it belongs. It is toxic, flammable, and violently explo-sive. CARBON TETRACHLORIDE is very toxic, causing chronic liver and kidney damage through skin absorption and inhalation. <u>Never</u> use it for cleanup. Solvents should <u>never</u> be used on the skin, since their defatting action dries out the skin, leaving it vulnerable to attack by a host of substances, such as resins. Even if this were not true, they are all severe systemic poisons which can be absorbed through the skin. ISOPROPYL ALCHOHOL (rubbing alchohol) will dissolve some uncured epoxies, and is one of a very few solvents which is safe to use on the skin. It is flammable, though, and its vapors can do damage, so use it sparingly, and with good ventilation.*

FIRE SAFETY should be on your mind at all times, since many materials used in boatbuilding are quite flammable, especially the popular polyesters. Keep a large dry-chemical fire extin-guisher handy at all times. Keep things tidy, so a small fire won't have fuel to feed on. Clean all spills promptly, and store all resin-soaked rags in a covered metal container away from combustibles. (Ed. note: remove trash regularly). Keep flam-

*Ed Note: Uncured epoxy dissolves in hot water quite nicely. More stubborn gelled epoxy can often be removed with detergents.

mable liquids in tightly closed metal containers. If you must occasionally make use of a glass container, protect it from breakage by storing it in a closed cupboard at ground level. DO NOT SMOKE, and never permit anyone in your shop to smoke. Locate your work well away from ignition sources: the furnace, water heater, clothes drier, etc. Don't forget that most gas appliances have pilot lights which can ignite flammable vapors without warning. Many of these vapors are heavier than air, and find their way to a basement pilot light via the stairs. Serious fires or explosions may result. Keep your ventilating operating to disperse the fumes whenever liquid containers are open, during layup, and throughout the curing process. (Editor's Note: when vacuum bagging, pumps must be vented externally during use. Solvents, especially acetone, should be used out of doors. Be certain that all electrical devices are equipped with power cords in good condition. Beware of overloaded extension cords, and avoid using cords with a wire of less than 16 guage. For protection against lethal electrical shock, use three-wire cords with a _good_ ground (preferably with a ground-fault interrupter) or double-insulated tools. Finally, remember that the curing of resins is exothermic, ie: heat is liberated by the process. Fires have been started by the heat given off by large plugs of curing mix.

PROTECTIVE DEVICES are the last line of defense against health and safety hazards and should be used only in conjunction with the controls mentioned above.

SKIN should always be protected when working with epoxies, as the consequences of sensitization are too serious to ignore. Protection is also important with polyesters, and makes sense for fiberglass as well. Skin protection starts with the proper clothing: a long sleeved shirt, plastic apron, and rubber or plastic _gloves_ long enough to cover the wrist area below the cuffs of the shirt.If gloves are unlined, you may wish to wear light cotton gloves underneath to absorb perspiration. A bathing cap or plastic bag should be worn over the hair when working inside the boat. Hands, wrists, and forearms should be liberally coated with _barrier cream_ even though gloves be worn. (Follow manufacturer's directions; Kerodex recommends #71 for epoxies) Since many creams are water soluble, their effectiveness diminishes after 2-4 hours, especially if you're sweating, so plan on making several applications during long work sessions. Skin is more resistant to dermatitis if it doesn't dry out, so use industrial skin conditioners such as Mine Safety Appliances Fend-X or Sugar Beet Products' SBS-40.

REMEMBER: THE WHOLE POINT IS TO AVOID ALL CONTACT WITH RESINS !

EYE PROTECTION should always be worn when working with dangerous liquids. The best splash and drip protection is obtained from a _chemical goggle_. These are usually made of plastic, with a soft facepiece that fits tightly around the eye area. Non-vented types give the best protection; vented types should have shielded vents. Be sure to get a type which can be worn with a respirator. When cutting and grinding, impact resistant eyewear meeting ANSI Z87.1 specs should be worn. Some chemical goggles meet these requirements.

IF LIQUID SOMEHOW GETS INTO YOUR EYE,FLUSH CONTINUOUSLY WITH COOL WATER AND GET TO A PHYSICIAN AT ONCE ! All shops should have available sufficient water in a squeeze bottle to flush an eye. (Ed. note)

RESPIRATORY protection is often misunderstood. For all its simplicity, a respirator is a complex and sophisticated device. Learn to use and maintain it, and it will protect you; treat it with contempt and apathy, and it is worse than nothing at all. Respirators should always be worn when working indoors, and only in conjunction with good ventilation. For our purposes, there are three basic types: the particulate respirator, which filters out dust and fibers from the air; the organic vapor respirator, which has an adsorbent cartridge for removing epoxy, polyester, and solvent vapors, and a combination type. For all-around use, the latter is ideal. A top-quality respirator has a half-facepiece mask which fits over the bridge of the nose and under the chin. (those that fit on the chin and lower lip are cheaper, but are less comfortable and tend to fit poorly) Twin cartridge units are superior to single cartridge types, in that they provide less breathing resistance and tend to last longer. Look for NIOSH (National Institute for Occupational Health and Safety) approval on any unit that you buy. Non-approved units may still be O.K., but it may become difficult to get parts for them in the future. BEWARE of cheap, non-approved respirators. Although there are a few inexpensive paper masks which are approved for use against non-toxic dusts, you're better off in the long run biting the bullet and spending money on a top-quality unit. There are no cheap vapor respirators which are any good.

The spray-painting respirator is a good one for boatbuilding. It is commonly available, and has an activated charcoal cartridge for vapors and a filter for dust. It is therefore suited for mixing, cutting, grinding, lay-up, and seaming - in short, any boatbuilding operation. If you want to go further, find a knowledgeable dealer and ask for an organic vapor unit with dust and mist prefilters. Filters must be replaced as they become clogged; vapor cartriges as they become saturated. Vapor cartridges last about eight hours in normal use, and must be stored in an airtight container or they will deteriorate just sitting around. People normally replace them when they begin to smell the vapors, but if you have a poor sense of smell, you'd better do things by the clock. Some combination units allow the use of either filters or cartridges alone, an economical feature since cartridges are expensive and deteriorate by absorbing moisture from the air, even when no vapors are present. For this reason, it is wise to purchse an inexpensive dust mask for use when cutting fiberglass or for hand-sanding of the layup.

CAUTION: Remember that a particulate respirator does not protect against vapors, and that vapor-only respirators are worthless against particulates. Also remember that while the units described above are good for epoxies, solvents, etc.they should NOT be used against other toxic materials (like pesticides) without first obtaining expert advice and special cartridges.

ALSO NOTE that leakage around the facepiece may occur (it takes pretty sophisticated equipment to evaluate a fit) and even a well-fitted facepiece is rated effective only up to ten times the accepted safe concentration of toxic materials. RESPIRATORS ARE NOT GAS MASKS, and should be used only in combination with good ventilation !!

FOR A RESPIRATOR TO DO ITS JOB, it must be kept clean. The unit should be washed at the end of each work session by removing the cartridge and filters and immersing the facepiece, straps and all, in warm, soapy water. Scrub gently to remove facial oils and dirt, then rinse with clean water and set out to dry. Before using it again, inspect it carefully. The inhalation valves are thin rubber discs which lie behind each cartridge filter on the inside of the facepiece; they function as check-valves to prevent moist, exhaled air from passing back through to the cartridge filter and degrading it. The exhalation valve is also a rubber disc located in the chin of the facepiece. Its function is to allow exhaled air to pass through while forcing inhaled air to go through the cartridge/filters. Both of these valves should lie flat and be free of debris. A single hair can cause a leakage of several per cent. The exhalation valve cover must always be in place to prevent leaks. Most respirators have gaskets under the cartridge/filters; check them to see that they are in good condition. The faceplace should be inspected for cracks or rotting, and the straps should be in good condition. If you find a defect, get a new part from the manufacturer. DO NOT attempt to modify or adapt the respirator to non-factory approved parts. When not in use, place in a plastic bag and keep in a cool, dry place. This will prolong its life substantially, as the rubber parts will be protected from attack by ozone and other pollutants. Be sure that the facepiece is not deformed in storage, or it will "take a set" and no longer fit.

SOURCES OF SAFETY EQUIPMENT are diverse. Respirators and chemical goggles can be found at the larger hardware stores, and at places like Sears and Wards. Hardware and auto supply stores stock waterless hand cleaner, while barrier creams and skin conditioners can be purchased at drug stores. Welding supply companies may also carry many of these items. In a big city, look in the yellow pages under "Safety Equipment." Many boat-building supply companies also stock what you need.

MANUFACTURERS are excellent sources of information, and should be consulted if your dealer is not knowledgeable, which is often the case. Major firms are:

*AO SAFETY PRODUCTS, American Optical Corp, Southbridge, Mass 01550 (Respirators, goggles, protective clothing, creams, conditioners)

*MINE SAFETY APPLIANCE CO, 600 Penn Center Blvd., Pbg., Pa. 15235 (With branch offices throughout the U.S. & Canada) - (Respirators, goggles, protective clothing, creams, and conditioners)(Also through J.R. Sweet)

SPECIAL PRODUCTS DEPT; AYERST LABORATORIES 685 3rd Ave., NYC 10017 (Kerodex Barrier Creams)

SUGAR BEET PRODUCTS CO., Saginaw, Michigan 48605 (Waterless hand cleaners & conditioning creams)

WELSH, a Textron Co., 9 Magnolia St., Providence, RI 02909 (Respirators & Goggles)

WILSON PRODUCTS DIVISION, ESB Co., 1985 Janice Ave, Melrose park, Ill., 60160 and 111 Sutter St, San Francisco, Calif. (Respirators & Goggles)

Most firms prefer to deal with their distributors. Those marked with an (*) will sell by mail order ($25 min). MSA also sells over the counter at its branch offices.

Editors note;The preceeding may seem overcautious. Most builders take little, if any precautions, and run sloppy, disorganized shops. There is no doubt that people can get away with violating these common sense rules; however, if you do and get into trouble because of it, DON'T SAY YOU DIDN'T KNOW !!

OBTAINING THE MOLD:

Most molds for whitewater kayaks, decked canoes, and racing hulls are owned by individuals, although occasionally canoe clubs, outfitter shops, and supply houses will have them to rent out. In some areas, they are simply unobtainable. In general, the more recent the design, the harder it is to find. Your local canoe club is the best place to meet other builders and obtain information on their whereabouts. If you don't know where your local club is, write the American Canoe Association, 7432 Alban Station Blvd., Suite B-226, Springfield, VA 22150.

The person responsible for the mold will want to know how much experience you've had (or who is helping you) and when and for how long you'll need to use the mold. You will want to know about the type of boat you'll be building, the condition of the mold, and the fee for its use.

EXPERIENCE: The owner is concerned with the safety of the mold, which probably took as much time to make as 4-6 boats. The MINIMUM VALUE is $1000. making it a rather expensive tool to rent to unknown builders. Manuals are fine, but the best way to learn is under the supervision of a competent builder. Many times a club member who is building will be happy to have you show up and help,and this will give you a good reference when your own time comes. Hiring a helper or arranging for experienced supervision (I have had several folks build in my garage while I stood by in case of trouble) is less common, but may work out better for you. Boatbuilding clinics are rarer, but not unusual in large, active canoe clubs. Whatever your resource, treat it with respect. For everyone who will lend a hand, dozens more just won't take the trouble.

TIME: A boat takes between 30 and 60 hours to build, depending on your skill and facilities. About half of this time requires help from a mold. You can turn a boat out in two days if you are very good and unafraid of long hours, but most people prefer to do the work over four or five evenings. Cure time may be important; polyester and some epoxies should be left alone for a day or two; some other epoxies will still be pretty "green" at this point. A full week (Sun to Sun) is a good estimate, and allows some margin for error.

COST: Mold fees run from $25-$50 per boat, with $20 being average. Some owners, fed up with late returns of molds, rent by the week. Others require a deposit (particularly of newcomers) to cover possible damage. Unless otherwise agreed, you are responsible for transporting the mold between the owner's shop and your own. BE FOREWARNED: honor your agreements and return the mold in good shape and on time. If you screw the owner, your story will be broadcast around the circuit until no one will care to rent to you again.

TRANSPORTATION damages many molds, so treat them like the expensive tools they are and take precautions. Use good racks; tie down securely with bow and sern lines in addition to direct lashing to the crossbar and follow the owner's instructions to the letter. Bolt-together molds should be transported fully attached; when the mold is carried in two halves, support each one to avoid warping or damaging them. Remember: damage to a mold in transit may be irreparable. Take no chances!

STORAGE: Keep the mold together (use 6-8 bolts) to prevent warping. Cover the cockpit hole to keep dirt, dust, and small animals out. If a boat does not have its own built-in frame, it should be stored in cradles. (You may store it on its side for short periods) Never store flat, as this may distort the hull and ruin future boats. Keep in an out-of the way place where it cannot be inadvertently damaged. Never store in the sun.

AGREEMENT ON MOLD USE:

This form, an adaptation of one used by John R.Sweet, spells out the duties of the mold user in a clear, concise way. Verbal agreements are fine, but it is best to have it all in black and white in case of conflicts.

As a precondition for the use of a canoe or kayak mold owned by, or in the care of _______________, Leasor, the following conditions are agreed to:

1. TRANSPORTATION OF THE MOLD: User is responsible for picking up the mold in_______________ and returning it to _______________ Leasor may on occasion be able to make delivery in conjunction with a race, meeting, or other event. Charge for this service will be ___ a mile if not out of the way.

The mold must be bolted together with 6-8 bolts whenever it is transported. Never transport unbolted. Do not put all the bolts in. Tie firmly to the vehicle, using <u>both</u> crossties to the racks <u>and</u> endties to the bumpers. Position it so that the rackbars are as close as possible to the plywood reinforcements on the mold. Use padding if necessary for the mold to ride well.

2. USE OF MOLD. The mold has been waxed. Clean with a damp rag, then apply a coat of Formula 5 mold wax and buff well. Handle the mold carefully during all operations. Be careful while trimming not to nick the flange (use a sharp knife; never a saw). Pull on plywood reinforcements to separate the mold (deck will usually release first) then pull on the boat to get it out. If it still resists release, encourage it with the release wedge (teflon) provided. Do not use a hammer without permission. If the boat should stick, <u>call</u> leasor before undertaking more drastic release measures. Remember that you are responsible for <u>all</u> <u>damage</u>.

When done with the mold carefully scrape all resin from the flanges wash the mold with warm water (do not use detergents or any kind c strong, abrasive cleanser) and buff dry. Apply a coat of Formula 5 mold wax, including the flanges, and buff dry. Bolt the mold firmly with 6-8 bolts.

3. SERIAL NUMBER: a serial number will be provided for each boat to be built. It must be laminated into the right edge of the stern deck so that it is legible on the outside of the boat. (Ed. note: this satisfies certain potential legal hassles). It is also useful to laminate in a tag with the owner's name and address.

4. OTHER CONSIDERATIONS: The user is responsible for the safe and prudent use of the mold in all respects, whether stated herein or not, and is responsible for all damage including loss or destruction of the mold. The value of the mold is at least $300 and can be as much as $1000. A nominal deposit will be charged, and will be refunded upon the prompt return of the mold in good condition. The deposit may be retained in whole or part by the leasor if the mold is dirty or damaged; if parts or accessories are missing; if it is kept longer than agreed upon; or otherwise handled unsatisfactorily.

5. SPECIFIC CONDITIONS: This should cover the following:

1. Name of the mold and its value
2. Pickup and return dates
3. Fees or deposits collected
4. Number of boats to be constructed
5. Name, address, and phone number of the borrower

Copies of this agreement can be kept by each party to serve as a record/reciept.

I have read, understand, and agree to all the terms of this agreement.

(Signed) ____________________ Date ________

CHECKING OUT A MOLD:

Having said all this, there are probably a number of molds out there that you do not want to rent. Be especially wary if the owner does not treat it with the respect; they may know something you don't! The following are things to watch out for:

OUT OF DATE DESIGNS: All kayaks are not created equal, and given the hassles involved, you want to be sure that the one you're making is going to be a good one. While slightly outdated models or classic designs are great for beginners, avoid getting mixed up with some of the early experiments. Although the boats they spawned have long since died the molds, like dinasaur eggs, remain to bring these monstrosities back to life. The usual victim is someone who wants to build "a kayak" and doesn't understand the differences. Chances are that the mold owner is equally ignorant, as there just isn't enough money involved to attract a competent sheister. If you can't get intelligent answers, watch out !

TYPES OF MOLD: Regardless of design, keep this in mind: modern molds are built in two halves, with a "flange" along each edge to join the two halves together. This widened rim (from 2"-6" wide) will make your life a lot easier when seaming the boat, or when storing and transporting the mold. An unflanged mold presents a number of problems to a builder, and is much more easily damaged. Also keep in mind that modern molds split along the sides into deck and hull pieces. The side-by-side mold is a real nuisance to seam properly, and indicates an obsolete design.

If you have a choice, look at the contours. Some decks (particularly Lettmann designs) have all kinds of sexy ridges which require plenty of skill to lay up. Their purpose is to stiffen the deck (and to add sex appeal). Many mold-makers remove these ridges, to the great advantage of the novice builder.

CONDITION: A smooth inner surface is the key to an easy release. It is not unusual for molds to be badly damaged. When you pick up the mold, look it over, and ask the owner how to deal with any problems you see. This avoids nasty squabbles when the mold is returned later. Note major problems on the agreement. If extensive work is required to get the mold in shape, a reduction of the rental fee is in order. It is considered good form to return the mold clean and lightly waxed. Damage should be repaired (with permission of the owner) or pointed out on making the return. ALWAYS ASK before doing anything.

PREPARING THE MOLD:

The smoother the inner surface of the mold, the more easily it will give up the finished boat. A clean release saves time, and minimizes mold damage. The first step in this direction is to preserve the interior finish; the second is to remove any defects prior to building. Time spent preparing the mold pays dividends later, and makes the finished product that much nicer.

1) WIPE THE INNER SURFACE CLEAN with a lint-free, dirt-free cloth. If the mold is very dirty, rinse with water. Do not use soap; it screws up the wax. Sticky substances can be removed using fine steel wool. If wax build-up is excessive (unlikely) you may, with the permission of the owner, use styrene to remove it.

2) CHIPS AND CRATERS can be temporarily filled with hot melted candle wax smoothed into place with your fingertips. With the permission of the owner, you can do a more permanent job with a high-quality auto body putty (Bondo) which is sanded flush with successive applications of 200, 400, and 600 grit wet sand paper. Knock resin blobs free with a squeegie.

3) A VERY ROUGH MOLD may have to be sanded all over to regain its smooth suface. Check with the owner first; its a time-consuming job which usually cancels out any mold fee. The roughness was caused by a partial failure of the mold release, and the owner may want to get satisfaction from the person responsible. As with the crevices, you will want to go over the entire surface with 200, 400, and 600 grit paper with rinses between each grade. Deep scratches may require a short application of medium grade paper if they are too shallow to fill.

CAUTION: A "reconditioned" mold is like a new mold. The first several boats are the hardest to remove, and demand extra wax and PVA. Stay away from the more tenacious systems (epoxy and vinylester) until the mold has been "conditioned."

NOTE: Using power tools inside the mold requires superhuman skill. Don't even try it unless you own the mold!

APPLYING RELEASE AGENTS:

The next step is to coat the inner surface of the mold with a hard paste wax. Do not use any wax containing silicones, or any "cleans n' shines" liquids without the consent of the owner, as these may make it impossible to use PVA. Only use a pure paste wax with a high Carnuba content. Since different release agents may not live with each other in harmony, smart mold owners sell their own release agents when they rent the mold, and give precise directions as to their use.

DIRECTIONS FOR WAXING: A new or rented mold should be given 4-5 coats of wax; 2-3 will suffice thereafter if the mold has not been handled or stored correctly. Apply each layer evenly, using a clean, soft rag. Pay special attention to the flanges, edges, bow and stern tips, and any other easily-missed spots. Wipe off excess immediately. Allow to dry. Buff with a clean bath towel. When the drag on the towel dissapears, you're done. Buff extra hard wherever drag is felt. Then apply another coat. Do not use power buffing equipment; it melts the wax and leaves invisible gaps. When you're done, a towel should slide easily from one end of the mold to the other.

NOTE ON WAXING: Wax build-up can be a problem, especially for older molds. Some people inadvertantly contribute to this by adding excessive layers of wax "just to be safe". A well broken-in mold may only require a single layer of wax. Follow the mold owner's directions, as removing excess wax with wax remover and rewaxing is annoying.

PVA LIQUID is then applied to a waxed mold to create an additional thin protective barrier to the resin. While not necessary for all systems, it is essential for most epoxies and vinylesters. In some cases, multiple layers will be needed ! The best way to apply it is to spray it on, but this requires a lot of skill. Most people use a clean, soft cloth, a fine brush, or a small-celled sponge. Use long, overlapping, unidirectional strokes. Since PVA is water soluble, it must not be dripped on or even touched. Overnight drying in a dust-free environment is recommended whenever possible.

VARIOUS SPRAYS are on the market. They can be highly effective, but many contain silicones which render PVA useless. Since an unfortunate combination could ruin a mold, I recommend the use of only one release system at a time. Clean the mold off with specially formulated mold cleaners if wax builds up too much.

Since the idea of a mold release is to get a thin, smooth barrier between the boat and the mold, the poorer the surface, the more wax and PVA will be required. Use extra care with raunchy molds, and keep rags contaminated with strange chemicals elsewhere. It's a good idea not to even touch a waxed mold, as this may break the coating without knowing it.

CUTTING THE CLOTH:

PATTERNS are needed to cut cloth for boatbuilding. If only one boat is going to be made, you may want to lay the cloth in lengthwise and trim off the excess. For more than one boat, you'll need a pattern and a cutting table. With good patterns, sharp, heavy-duty shears, and a firm working surface several layers (one boat's worth) can be cut out at the same time. (Hint: do this during waxing, while you're waiting for the wax to dry).

If the mold owner did not lend you his patterns, here's how to make your own: take a well-behaved fabric, such as 10 oz fiberglass or style 181 Kevlar and lay it in the mold. Adjust to remove all wrinkles, cut accurately along the flange, then transfer to a more permanent material (6 ml polyethylene film or 40 lb Kraft wrapping paper). Mark each piece clearly with the name of the mold, whether it is the hull or deck, and which end is the bow and which is the stern. This saves considerable embarassment later. The cut piece of cloth can be saved for use in your layup.

Cutting tables are hard to find. Ping-pong tables are excellent. The floor, swept and washed, can be used as a last resort. Lay plastic film down if possible to keep dirt out. The cloth should be rolled stern to bow, the bow marked, the roll tagged as to the nature of the part (deck or hull) prior to storage. I recommend that a 2"-3" leeway be allowed until you are sure of your pattern. Later, you can cut the material more exactly.

The cutting technique you will find most effective depends on the cost of the material as well as its width. The thriftier metheods are more time consuming, and are not always justified by the savings. (The biggest problem is to keep the different pieces in order !) My own approach is to be very thrifty with Kevlar, but to choose the easiest approach for other fabrics.

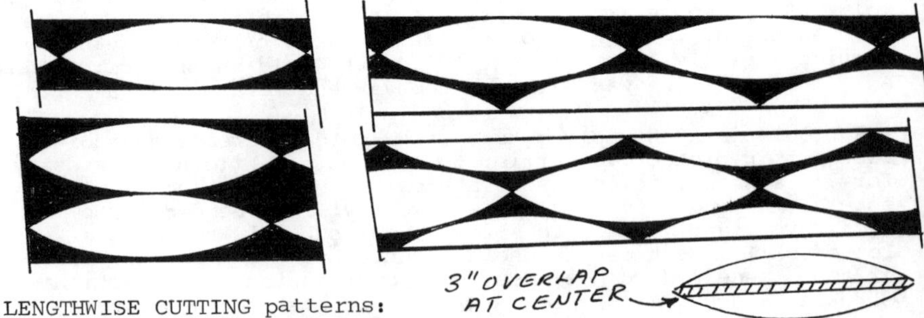

LENGTHWISE CUTTING patterns:

Can be modified according to the width of the fabric. Is very thrifty if an overlap at center is used; otherwise, it is quite wasteful of some widths of cloth. For maximum savings on this and other techniques, cut the pieces as close together as possible. Remove the selvage (finished edge) on halves for hand layup; keep it for vacuum-bagging.

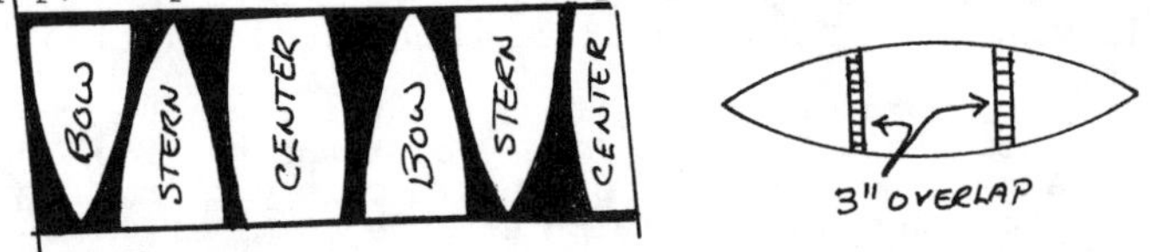

CROSSCUTTING is extremely thrifty, but multiple overlaps do occur. To avoid rapid changes in flexibility which can create a stress riser and cause shear failure, do not allow overlaps to occur on the same place in different layers. The overlaps act as ribs, and will be of some help in stiffening flexible boats. As before; remove the selvage for hand layups, as air bubbles may form behind it which are difficult to remove.

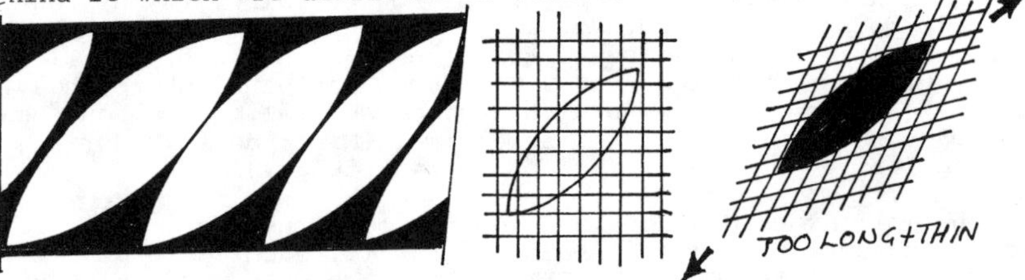

BIAS CUTTING is thrifty, but has a major drawback: It is very easy to pull the cloth transversly across the weave when handling the cloth, causing the weave to collapse and pulling the piece out of shape so it will no longer fit the mold. NOT RECOMMENDED for inexperienced builders !

SAVE ALL SCRAPS for reinforcing. Store flat; wrinkled cloth traps air bubbles and cannot be used without a hassle. Roll sizeable pieces up on a tube. MARK the bow and stern of all cut pieces, and store rolled until ready to use.

THE OVERLAPS discussed above do not have much effect on the overall strength of the boat - so long as you plan things so that stress risers do not form. There is no advantage to having a continuous layer <u>except</u> on the outside. there it may prevent air bubbles (always a problem with overlaps) and ruin the finish. If you <u>must</u> overlap in one place (ie: the keel) more than once, make one a 2" overlap, the other a 4" overlap.

CLOTH CUTTING IN THE MOLD is the metheod preferred by one-time builders who don't want to go to the trouble of making patterns. Here are a few hints: First, don't try any of the fancy layouts described previously unless you're looking for trouble. Second, take the time to lay all the cloth flat in the mold before cutting. An extra hand can be indispensable here, as the cloth is slippery and tends to shift around at the wrong time. Lastly, cut the layers first, then lay up. Doing both at the same time risks resin damage to unused cloth, and small trimmings may get lodged in the layup, causing air bubbles that are very difficult to remove.

SMALL PRODUCTION SHOPS AND AMBITIOUS CLUB PROGRAMS will want to be as efficient as possible. However, when cutting materials for several boats at a time, keeping the pieces organized can be a real challenge. Any heavy duty 12" shear can cut multiple layers of fiberglass; Clark Associates recommends using Weiss 41S shears on Kevlar or multiple layers of polypropylene, nylon, or other synthetics. Even when expensive ($50+) scissors are used, keeping them sharp enough to cut Kevlar can be difficult. Jesse Whittemore recommends investing in a scissor sharpener; it can make even cheap shears sharp enough to cut Kevlar for a short time. In a pinch, you can sharpen scissors with a flat bastard file if you follow the bevel angles carefully.

ALL CUT MATERIALS, including reinforcements, should be carefully labelled and rolled before storage to prevent embarrasing mistakes during lamination. Always mark the bow and stern ends where appropriate; masking tape labels are easily removed if applied lightly.

REINFORCEMENT PATTERNS:

People reinforce canoes or kayaks to increase strength and rigidity at key points. The increase in rigidity happens regardless of whether you want it to or not, and herein lies the problem. A sudden change of flexibility created when several layers of reinforcement end simultainiously produce a STRESS RISER; shear stress will concentrate at this point and cause damage. Avoid this by making certain that your boat's thickness does not change by more than one layer every 3 inches. A series of overlapping reinforcements will flex smoothly and permit the laminate to distribute stress evenly for long life.

Below are reinforcement patterns for high volume boat hulls:

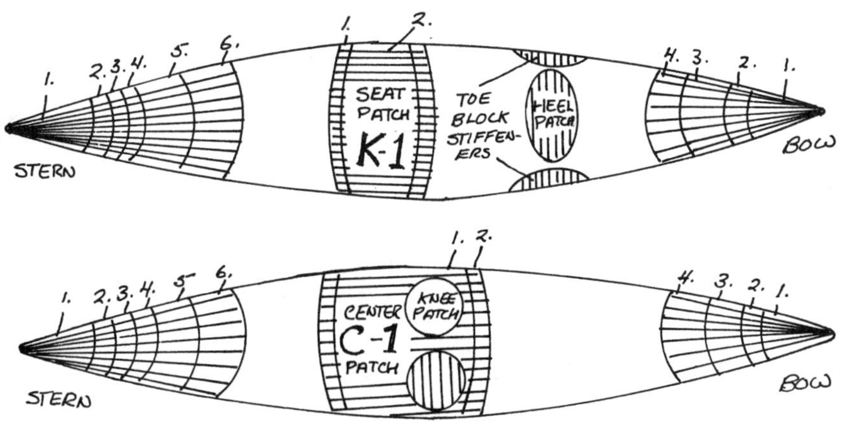

Below are the reinforcement patterns for low-volume boat hulls:

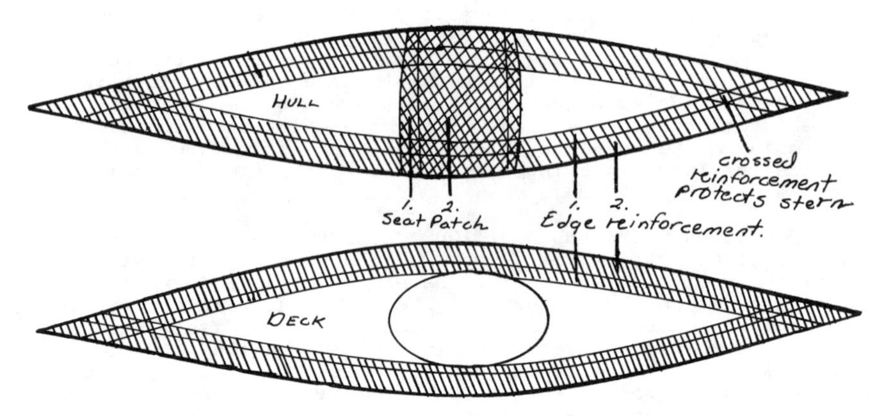

EXPLAINATIONS:

STERN AND BOW PATCHES are important to all whitewater boats, especially high-volume designs with well-defined keels. 2-3 layers are sufficient on lightweight boats; 4-5 on cruisers, 6-8 on expedition weight versions. Fewer layer are needed in the bow than in the stern. Please note how the low-volume hull is patched differently, since it has no defined keel. Use Kevlar or nylon for reinforcement.

CENTER PATCHES increase rigidity and allow for greater wear. One purpose is to prevent "oilcanning" under pressure. One "glass" layer is necessary on lightweight boats; foam core material is often substituted here to save weight. 2-3 layers will be needed on cruising kayaks and most C-1's. The added width of C-1's and C-2's has head to extensive use of ribs and keels, particularly on the high-volume cruising and wildwater racing designs.

EDGE REINFORCEMENT is used primarily in low volume designs. Squirt boat pioneer Jesse Whittemore feels that this contains the damage at the seam caused by the stress of spin-turns and enders. This is not necessary on high-volume boats which have less stress put on the seams. Note how the patches overlap to form stern/bow patches . Fiberglass or synthetics may be used.

HEEL AND KNEE PATCHES are used in cruising boats to deal with interior wear. Footbrace stiffeners provide extra strength and rigidity where footbraces are bolted in. This is especially important with lightweight boats, whose thin skins can be torn when bolted-in footbraces absorb severe impacts. Use fiberglass.

APPLY REINFORCEMENTS between the layers of the boat. Most builders put them just under the last layer, although those using heavy stern or bow layers may wish to distribute it between several layers. Racing boats use keels and core materials in place of reinforcement, as discussed elsewhere.

DECK REINFORCEMENT:

Decks are usually laid up a layer lighter than hulls. Since they take less abuse, reinforcement is designed to increase rigidity rather than strength. The cockpit rim, for example, takes a lot of pressure when entering or leaving the boat. Add two layers of fiberglass here. "Ender patches" are added by people who enjoy standing up on end; edge reinforcement makes sense for squirt boats, and additional tip patches provide added strength at the bow and stern to deal with collisions. Use fiberglass for reinforcement.

BREAK-AWAY COCKPITS FOR KAYAKS:

In-boat entrapment has emerged as a leading cause of accidental death among kayak paddlers. Many experienced paddlers prefer fiberglass boats because their increased rigidity can prevent some wraps and, in the event of a severe pin, the kayak will break apart, allowing the paddler to escape.

Phoenix Products, the last major manufacturer of fiberglass kayaks, pioneered the "break-apart" concept. Much oftheir work involves destructive testing under simulated pins, and to be 100% certain you have to test your boats this way. But you can get 95% assurance by simply laying up the entire cockpit area and the deck up to the footbraces with fiberglass. No Kevlar, nylon, or other synthetics should be used except for a narrow strip along the seam line. Fiberglass is brittle, and will fracture in a severe pin. Combined with a wall, this will increase you margin of safety when compared to roto-molded construction.

C-1 and C-2 entrapments are due mainly to the deck lowering down on the victim's thighs and feet, trapping him in place. Break-apart cockpits are not particularly useful here.

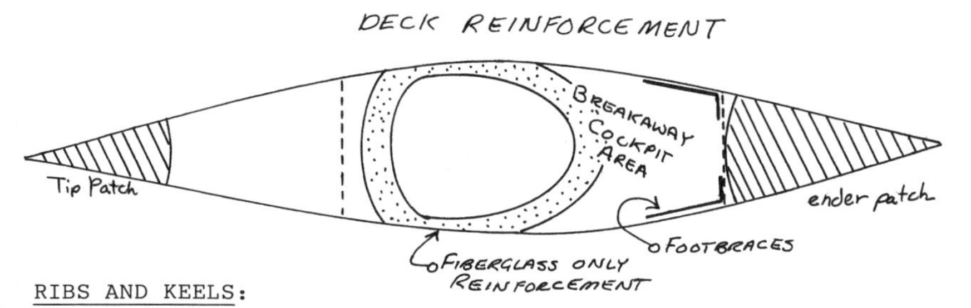

RIBS AND KEELS:

Ribs and keels increase rigidity without adding strength or weight. It is especially useful when making racing boats or when increasing the rigidity of C-1's, C-2's, and open canoes. Adding these structures is quite time consuming, and few manufacturers will do it. Carbon fiber roving was quite popular in the early 70's, and is quite easy to handle; cellulose acetate twine (a common type of binder's twine) is almost as good and very inexpensive. Bill McKnight uses saturated lengths of nylon rope covered with fiberglass tape. Steve Rock recommends Dynaframe or Airex foam strips with adhesive backing, made especially for this purpose. You may be able to get by with appropriately-shaped pieces of adhesive-backed weatherstripping of the appropriate shape.

These materials provide a "form" over which a layer or two of fiberglass is then laid. The material is shaped into a rounded contour to minimize air bubbles, then glued in place if needed with contact cement. Cover with fiberglass tape or (better) bias-cut strips of fiberglass cloth. 1-2 layers is plenty! Keels are usually 3/4"-1" wide and ribs about 1/3 that size.

KEEL
RIB
NOTE: RIBS DO NOT CROSS SEAM!
FIBERGLASS
FOAM OR WOOD
RIB CROSS SECT

As foam core technology has developed, interest in ribs has waned. You don't see them used much anymore.

HAND LAYUP PROCEDURES:

Preparation is the hardest part of any job. Now that you've laid the groundwork, its time to start building.

MIX THE RESIN according to your supplier's instructions, paying particular attention to pot size. It takes about twelve ounces of resin (1½ pints) to saturate the initial layer of a moderate volume slalom kayak; 16 ounces (2 pints) will handle a C-2. This is a good amount to start with. If using one of the "esters", mix this batch a bit slow. You can always add more catalyst to speed the reaction later if conditions warrent. If you can't make batches this size without the resin going off, consult your supplier. It had better be MIGHTY GOOD STUFF to compensate you for the hassle.

WHEN USING PIGMENT, mix the entire batch of pigmented resin at once. This insures a perfect color match. Trying to get "a little more resin" the same tint as an existing batch is almost impossible, so make plenty. If you are doing the deck and hull at the same time, the resin for the outer layer of both pieces must be mixed together. If you want the seat to match, add an extra half-pint. Although only the first layer is usually pigmented (except for those wanting a very dark boat), any extra resin can be easily worked into succeding layers without affecting the cosmetics. If you're using more than one color, be sure to make enough of each batch.

APPLYING THE GELL LAYER:

The outside of your canoe or kayak is important from the standpoint of appearance and wear. Most experienced builders begin the layup by carefully applying a coat of pigmented resin to the inner surface of the mold. This has three functions: to give the finished craft a perfectly smooth appearance; secong, to increase wear by protecting the laminate's outer layer of cloth, and lastly to guard against pinhole leaks and other interlaminar imperfections. Pay special attention to the edges, bow and stern ends, deck convolutions, and other hard-to-see places when applying this layer.

A true "gelcoat" is a specially-formulated layer of resin used to produce a high gloss on factory-produced products. It is allowed to "gell", or set up to a jello-like consistancy before additional layers are applied. These formulations are to brittle for use in whitewater boats, so boatbuilders use a single layer of laminating resin instead. What happens next is controversial. Some allow the layer to gell, others wait for a cure. A few even permit each layer to set up before applying the next. I feel that these extreme procedures are overkill; designed to cope with pinholes and patterning caused by using resin not modified by thixotropes. With a properly formulated system, letting the outer layer gell is quite sufficient.

My own technique is to put down the initial layer of resin and immediately procede with the lamination. It is faster, and seems to produce good results. And, since the excess will be absorbed by the cloth, you don't have to be concerned with removing drips and puddles as you would with a "real" gelcoat. If you find the resin running down the sides of the mold without covering it, you need to add thixotrope to prevent further difficulties. If you don't,th problems with the gel layer will be followed by pinholes along the edge of the boat which result when the resin runs out of the cloth.

At the other extreme of technique, I have run into several builders who swear that all you need to do is lay in the first layer of cloth and apply the resin, without any initial layer at all. A few even do this to several layers at once. While experts using very thin resins may get away with this, the average person will be left with an unspeakable mess. I'll never try it this way!

On another note, John Schriner of New Wave Kayaks warns that "alligatoring", described on page 15, can result if a layup procedes on a partially set gelcoat. If you are allowing the resin to set up, wait until it is firm. If it pulls away when you touch it with your fingers, you need to wait longer. Boat fabricator Steve Gillette of Georgia reports that air bubbles and other imperfections are easily removed from the gelcoat as you are waiting for it to cure. A good idea for those seeking the best possible finish.

My recommendation: apply the resin and procede directly to the layup unless you are looking for the ultimate in perfect finishes.

Commercial operations apply resin to the laminate with spray guns. These are out of reach of the average ameteur fabricator, but a fast alternative is to use a milk jug cut as shown. You can pour or brush on the resin as needed. Since the working time of the resin is much longer when spread out than it is when concentrated in the pot, it pays to apply it as fast as possible. But don't add too much unless you want a "river pig".

LAYING IN THE CLOTH requires skill and patience. The preferred technique is to 1) pour some resin into the mold and spread it out into a thin layer 2) drop the cloth on top of it and work it into place as well as you can 3) add additional resin to fully saturate the cloth and 4) check quality and remove excess resin. The idea is to saturate the cloth from the bottom up as well as the top down, entrapping less air and allowing the work to proceed faster. It is the main reason that I personally do not allow the gel coat to set up, or allow individual layers to gel before doing the next.

THE OVERALL ROUTINE IS AS FOLLOWS:

1) Lay down the gelcoat.
2) Put the first layer of cloth in place. Work with brush or plasticator until it lies down flat. Don't worry too much about wrinkles for now. The resin will soak through some areas, leaving others dry.
3) After you've done all you can to remove wrinkles, start applying resin to the unsaturated areas. Unless the resin is very thin, it won't be absorbed right away. Don't panic; this can't be rushed. Resist the urge to flood the area with resin. Work on another part of the boat, and then come back. Redistribute excess resin found dripping or puddling to areas that need it; return it to the pot if necessary. Partly saturated cloth is dark in color, with the weave being slightly visible. If you can't make out the texture of the cloth, try removing more resin.
4) Check the laminate for complete saturation. Remove wrinkles and air bubbles, and work on the ends of the boat. Remove major puddles and drips, leaving a thin layer of resin on the surface to help saturate the next layer.

5) Drop in the next layer and repeat the process. The reinforcing strips go in between layers. Once the last layer is in place, remove all possible excess resin.

THIS IS A TIME CONSUMING PROCESS, especially for novices. I'd allow about 3-4 hours per half the first time. As newcomers have to work more slowly, be sure that the pot life of your formulation matches your skills.

The following handling techniques are helpful:

LONG LENGTHS OF CLOTH can be a problem to handle. First, locate the "bow" and "stern" on both the cloth <u>and</u> the mold (sounds silly, but people <u>have</u> put whole boats together backwards!). Start at one end, and roll the cloth into place. Several people, working in unison, can "drop" a piece in place very quickly. See that the piece is centered, and the ends lined up, before pressing it against the mold. Crosscutting produces shorter pieces which are easily handled by one person. Fold each in half lengthwise, lay the fold along the keel-line, and drop into place. NOTE: For a smooth finish, the outer layer should be continuous.

TO REMOVE WRINKLES, start at the center and work towards the ends. First work the wrinkles to the edge of the mold, then along the sides to the bow or stern where they can be worked out more easily. Try to work the major ones out as you set the cloth in place, then do the minor ones while applying resin from the top.

STERN

"ROLLING IN"

WRINKLE ROUTES

AIR BUBBLES can be formed by 1) air under wrinkles 2) air trapped in the resin 3) dirt trapped under the cloth. Since an air pocket forms a gap between two layers, delamination will result if they are not removed. Shine a light underneath translucent molds for greater visibility. Ordinary air bubbles appear as light, circular areas; if there is a speck of dirt, it will show up plainly, too. Dirt particles must be removed by peeling back the cloth before going any further. Then press down on the air bubbles with a brush or squeegie to remove them.

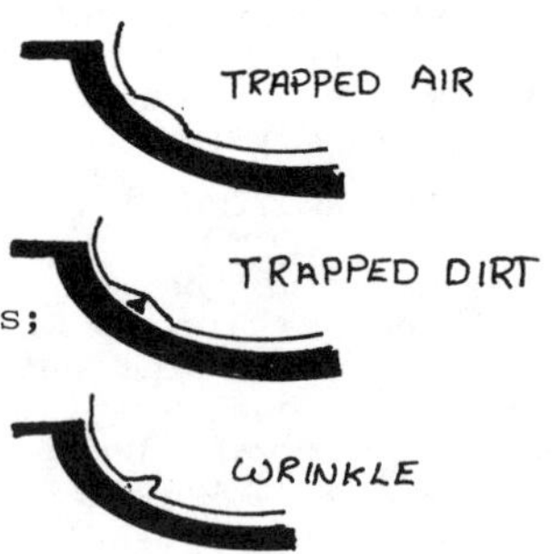

NOTE: Keep a clean shop. It saves time and hassle in the long run !!

A COMMON SITE FOR BUBBLES is along the edge of the mold, caused where the cloth curls over the edge and on to the flange. These cannot be removed until the offending cloth is trimmed flush with the surface of the flange. Once this is done, there is seldom any further problem.

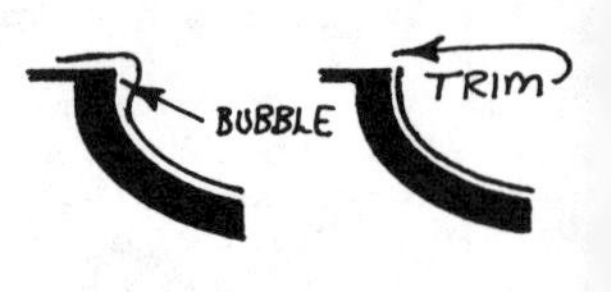

THE BOW AND STERN pose particular problems, and should be the last part laid up on each layer. In addition to wrinkles (to be discussed later), persistant air bubbles will form where the cloth "bridges" the bottom. The reason the cloth has "pulled away" from the mold is because it has been stretched. Push down along the sides, as shown, until the cloth falls into place and the bubble disappears. In extremely difficult cases, such as the bows of wildwater boats, consider laying the worst part up separately with bias-cut strips of cloth.

FLATWATER RACING BOATS have extremely sharp bows which cannot be laid up by conventional techniques. Builders use a mold with the bow slit with a saw cut. The cloth used in the layup is extended through that cut and trimmed. The bow is then clamped together, and after curing becomes solid. There is some loss of strength, but this is not a problem with this kind of boat.

THE BEST TOOL FOR REMOVING EXCESS RESIN is a plasticator, or squeegie. When you draw the blade firmly across the laminate, any extra resin in the cloth will be squeezed out in front of it. Concentrate on drips and puddles; the latter tends to build up at the bottom of the mold.

CAUTION: Beware of removing too much resin ! You must leave enough to fill not only the fibers of the weave, but also the spaces in between. Excessive pressure on the squeegie can leave the laminate under-saturated, causing pinholes or weak spots. If the cloth turns white or appears porous, add more resin and proceed less vigorously. A perfectly saturated laminate will appear uniformly dark, with the weave pattern barely visible. Puddles of resin may appear at the bottom of the hull or deck. These should be removed unless you are going to add the next layer immediately.

Epoxy resins seem to require the most vigorous squeegie work, particularly the thick polyamid systems. Layups using vinyl-ester, on the other hand, seem to require extra resin. A laminate that appears fully saturated when wet will often be undersaturated when cured; the only way to prevent this is to leave a thin surface "film" of "extra" resin.(NOT puddles). Polyester resin falls between the two extremes.

WRINKLES CAN BE MOVED by pulling the cloth in front of them with a plasticator or paint-brush (for tight areas, such as the bow or stern, paintbrushes work better than squeegies) Eventually they will be flattened or worked out the edges. Use firm, overlapping strokes. Sometimes too vigorous squeeging will cause a wrinkle to form in front of the plasticator. To remove it, just pull in the other direction until the cloth lies flat. Additional resin will lubricate the process in dry areas.

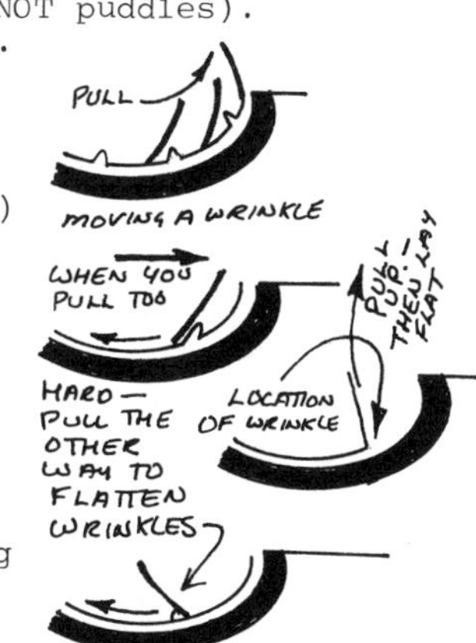

WARNING: Do not try to squeegie gelled resin. It is impossible and often results in wrinkling several layers at once (a horrible mess).

WRINKLES can be removed in several ways:

The cloth can be lifted away from the rest of the laminate until the wrinkle is lifted out, then laid flat. This technique is best for removing large lengthwise wrinkles at the center of the boat.

When wrinkles are concentrated in the bow or stern, they can be removed by determined trial and error. But sometimes the cloth has been so badly pulled out of shape that it cannot be made to lie in place. If this happens, try to gather the material into one large wrinkle. Using old scissors, cut the wrinkle down to its apex. The cloth will lay flat when you overlap the edges. Since this weakens the boat, and may complicate the laying-up of subsequent layers, do it only as a last resort.

OPAQUE LAMINATES, such as those containing Kevlar or heavily-pigmented resin, are more difficult to work with. The color changes causeed by cloth saturation or the presence of air bubbles are much less pronounced. Extra alertness, reinforced by a light shining through the mold from the outside, may be helpful. Novices are advised to avoid these materials the first time around.

The next section deals with vacuum-bagging technique. Those not interested in this can proceed to Page 79, the section on trimming.

VACUUM BAGGING TECHNIQUE:

This section is taken primarily from notes submitted by Steve Rock, one of the pioneers in this technique. Additional material from John Brown and Clark and Associates has been integrated into Rock's text.

WHAT IS VACUUM BAGGING:

Vacuum bagging is a process whereby the cloth and resin laid into a mold is covered by a plastic sheet, forming a sealed compartment from which air can be evacuated via a pump . As the bag collapses (due to atmospheric pressure), the laminate is compressed between it and the mold. As pressure increases, excess resin as well as air can be removed.

ADVANTAGES:

1. Vacuum bagging produces lighter and stronger boats than conventional hand lay-up techniques because:

    a) It permits the use of specialized, high-strength fibers which are totally unsuited to hand lay-up because of stiffness, tightness of weave, or a tendancy to absorb too much resin. It also allows the use of high-performance, undiluted resins which are too thick for contact lamination.

    b) Vacuum bagging increases the fiber content and decreases the amount of resin in the layup. Unless carried to extremes, this increased cloth-to-resin ratio increases strength per unit of weight. More cloth can be put into a given boat without adding additional pounds.

    c) A properly bagged boat has less air in the laminate than one laid up by hand. This produces a more homogeneous, higher-quality layup with greater resistance to fatigue and delamination.

2. Vacuum-bagging reduces resin contact by putting the bag between you and the resin. This reduces the health hazzard of the more commonly-used resins, and allows experienced builders to use more toxic, but higher strength materials which they would not consider for hand lay-up.

3. Vacuum bagging can be used to add foam cores or extensive rib systems to produce ultra-lightweight, high-performance craft. The pressure of the bag eliminates the trapped air which causes problems for contact laminators, allowing these additions to become integral parts of the layup.

DISADVANTAGES:

1. Increased complexity, with more opportunities for mistakes, makes this procedure more demanding for the builder. A novice can easily ruin a boat, rather than, as is the case with most hand layups, end up with a paddleable mistake. Unless you are highly experienced home craftsman, competent help is essential.

2. Loss of rigidity. Stiffness in a laminate is primarily a function of thickness. Small reductions in thickness greatly increase flexibility. By pressing out excess resin, vacuum bagging cuts thickness by 40-50%, making the laminate lighter and considerably less rigid. This means that you cannot vacuum bag a boat and have it come out both lighter and as stiff as a similar one laid up by hand. Careful laminate design is needed to overcome differences in construction technique.

A well-designed vacuum-bagged lamiate deals with this excessive flexibility by using additional layers of cloth in the laminate. This builds up the thickness needed to restore rigidity, but since there is more fiber per unit of resin in the cured part, the result is a denser, heavier hull. Although this hull is tougher than a hand-layup could produce, weight is important too. Weight loss is obtained by using the less dense synthetic fabrics (Nylon, Polypro, CAP, and especially KEVLAR) in preference to the denser fiberglass cloths. This allows increased thickness and fiber content without increased weight. Nylon, and Polypropylene <u>must</u> be clad with fiberglass or Kevlar to optimize rigidity.

To sum up: when two similar laminates are used, an all-fiberlass bagged layup will be lighter and more flexible than one laid up by hand. Adding an extra layer of fiberglass regains the stiffnes but adds extra weight. The addition of a synthetic layer allows you to replace the stiffness lost while at the same time producinc a boat which is lighter than that laid up by hand. This also produces a denser, tougher, and more costly boat.

3. Vacuum-bagging is a more costly process due to the increased number of layers used and the need for additional equipment and materials.

MOLD PREPARATION:

Vacuum-bagging does not require special molds, but several features will make the process easier. They are as follows:

1. A wide flange: 2" minimum; 4-6" preferred. Without this flange, the entire mold will have to be inserted into a bag, which is quite a job. Adding a flange is a major task.

2. The cockpit opening must be sealed closed. The best way is to fiberglass it over permanently, but this means that an additional vacuum connection should be made in the opening and makes in-the-mold seaming impossible. The opening can be covered by an airtight sheet of bag material, but in the case of kayak molds with hanging seats this means that the "chimney" around the cockpit opening must be puttied up level to provide an attachment point. This can be done temporarily, which is an advantage on borrowed molds. Putting the entire mold inside a vacuum bag is a less desirable option, as it is complex and messy.

3. Several holes should be drilled in the flange so that the pump can be securely and reliably attached via hoses. Once the hole is drilled, a pipe of the proper outside diameter for your system can be inserted and fiberglassed in place.

   If the mold owner will not give you permission to drill these holes (which do not in any way interfere with the normal use of the mold) buy two plastic T-fittings and wire them into place along the flange using the existing bolt holes. Put plenty of sealant under and around the "T" to make it "vacuum-tight." Refer to the "Preparations" section for details on exact location.

NOTE: Permanent modifications to an existing mold must not be made without the consent of the mold owner. Unless you have made other arrangements, return the mold <u>exactly</u> as it was recieved.

ADDITIONAL TOOLS NEEDED:

VACUUM PUMPS can be bought new for 100-200 dollars, but it is often possible to borrow one from a lab, buy a used one at a surplus store, or salvage one from a refrigerator or car air conditioner. Pumps are rated two ways: by vacuum and by volume. Vacuum refers to the extent that the pump can remove air, measured in inches of mercury (standard atmospheric pressure is 30") The volume of a pump refers to the amount of air moved at atmospheric pressure, measured in cubic feet per minute (CFM). The pump used in a vacuum-bagging setup should draw 15" Hg and have a minimum 3 cfm capacity. This is not very much, but ultra high volume or vacuum pumps are neither necessary nor even "better".

RESIN TRAPS are containers which catch excess resin before it can reach the pump, where it can do considerable damage. Any container will do if it can 1)withstand the pressures being used (most glass is not suitable; many light metal containers will collapse under vacuum) 2) can be tapped with vacuum-tight connections 3) can withstand the heat generated by a curing mass of resin (200+ degrees) and 4) has a minimum capacity of one gallon (two consecutive traps can be used in a pinch, but this increases the danger of leaks) The best traps are five-gallon LP gas cans with a pipe fitting tapped or epoxied in place. Five gallon tight-head drums reinforced with several layers of fiberglass cloth to prevent implosion are also recommended. Large lidless containers can be covered with plexiglass or metal plate, with inlet and outlet tubes affixed and sealed with epoxy, vacuum-bag sealant, or silicone rubber. The large capacity of the recommended containers reduces the danger of blockage due to the tendency of large masses of resin to foam as they cure, a process which increases the volume two or three times

THE VACUUM "BAG" is a sheet of tough, transparent, flexible plastic film such as 2 ml thick PVA sheet or 2 ml Capron. If neither of these are available, 6ml polyetheylene (available in some hardware stores) can be used. The latter is stiffer and more fragile than PVA. All bags must be treated and used with great care, since wrinkles are nuisance and punctures cannot be tolerated. PVA tends to absorb and lose moisture, particularly if stored indoors in winter or in places with a low humidity. If it seems brittle, leave it in an enclosure for a few days with a damp towel. The film wrinkes when overmoist, and is far more usable in this condition then when dry. Test by stretching it between your hands. Considerable force should be required to break it, and it should have no tendancy to rip. Polyethylene should never be used with polyester or vinylester resins.

SQUEEGIES used for vacuum bagging differ slightly from those used in hand lay-up. The best is a 3½"x3"x1/8" Teflon plate. Nylon, Polyethylene, and other soft plastics are good, but must be thicker (1/4") to be adequately rigid; the thick end of regular auto body squeegies are fine. ALL CORNERS MUST BE ROUNDED, AND ALL EDGES SANDED with fine sandpaper to avoid puncturing the bag.

VACUUM BAG SEALANT is a ribbon of gooey rubber rolled on a wax paper backing. It is laid on the flange, and the plastic sheet is pressed down on top of it, creating a vacuum-tight joint. The ribbon of sealant is 1/2" wide by 1/8" thick; sixty feet will be needed for a white water boat. Resin, dust, and other contaminants must be kept clear, as they can ruin the sealant. A good sealant can be easily stripped from the mold. In production operations, doubled layers of used sealant may be used for 3-5 additional parts. Buy from a vacuum-bagging supplier, or (in quantity) #3168, 1/16"x1/2", from Schnee-Moorhead in Irving, Texas. In a pinch, plate glass or sheet metal sealant can be obtained from the appropriate dealer.

MANIFOLDS/BLEEDERS: A manifold is a tube attached along the length of the flange, staying under the bag between the sealant and the layup. Its purposes are as follows: a) to keep the bag from sealing off the vacuum hose where it enters the system b) to collect and remove excess resin as it is forced out of the layup. There are several possible materials for manifolds. A stiff hose at least ½" in diameter (polyethylene pipe) which cannot be compressed by the vacuum works well. It must be drilled or kerfed (a kerf is a saw cut halfway through the tubing) at frequent intervals along its entire length so that resin can flow easily into the tubing. Plastic tubing needs to be flexed repeatedly to eliminate set-in curl. Sand all kerfs, drill holes and tubing ends to remove any sharp edges which could puncture the bag. Screen door extension springs also make good manifolds, and their reduced bulk is welcome where narrow flanges are present. Stretch the springs so that there is no more than 3/16" between each wire (½" diameter spring), then place several springs end-to-end to cover the full length of the flange. Bend the ends of the wire back and out of the way so that the bag will not be punctured.

VACUUM TUBING is used to connect the components of the system. It should have a minimum inside diameter of 1/4" and fit the mold, pump, and trap fittings tightly. Smart builders will design the system so that all fittings are the same size. The best source of vacuum hose is an auto supply store, which carries tubing made especially for this purpose. Other types of tubing will collapse under vacuum. Fittings can be found there or at scientific supply houses.

If your pump does not already have them built-in, a bleeder valve and vacuum guage must be added. The bleeder regulates the vacuum by letting in air. An ordinary plumbing valve attached to a T-Fitting works well. Place the two close together so that the vacuum can be monitored as you operate the bleeder.

RELEASE CLOTH is a heat-treated fabric laid on top of the last layer of a vacuum-bagged layup. It is treated so that resin can't stick to it, and it will be pulled off once the resin is cured. Its major purpose is to leave a rough surface (in contrast to the normal smooth inside surface on vacuum-bagged parts) to make it possible to seam and outfit a boat without sanding. The release cloth (Peel-Ply is the trade name for special cloth treated with a release agent; regular nylon laminating cloth also works well) is placed along the seam line and where outfitting must be done. In dry-layup vacuum-bagging, this material will have to be basted in place. Use light cotton thread so that the release cloth can be easily pulled away.

SPECIFIC RECOMMENDATIONS by W.A. Clark and Assoc., Boulder, Colo.

VACUUM PUMP: Gast Model 1022, a rotory-vane, motor-mounted, lubricated pump with built-in releif valve and vacuum guage.

RESIN TRAP: 5 Gallon tight-head drums; 22 guage or greater. Lighter weight drums can be used, but must be reinforced with four layers of glass fabric in varying widths wrapped around the center

PREPARATIONS FOR "BAGGING":

1. CONNECT THE MOLD TO THE PUMP: The vacuum line runs from the mold fittings to the resin trap and on from the traps to the pump. Be sure that the hoses from the mold hang straight

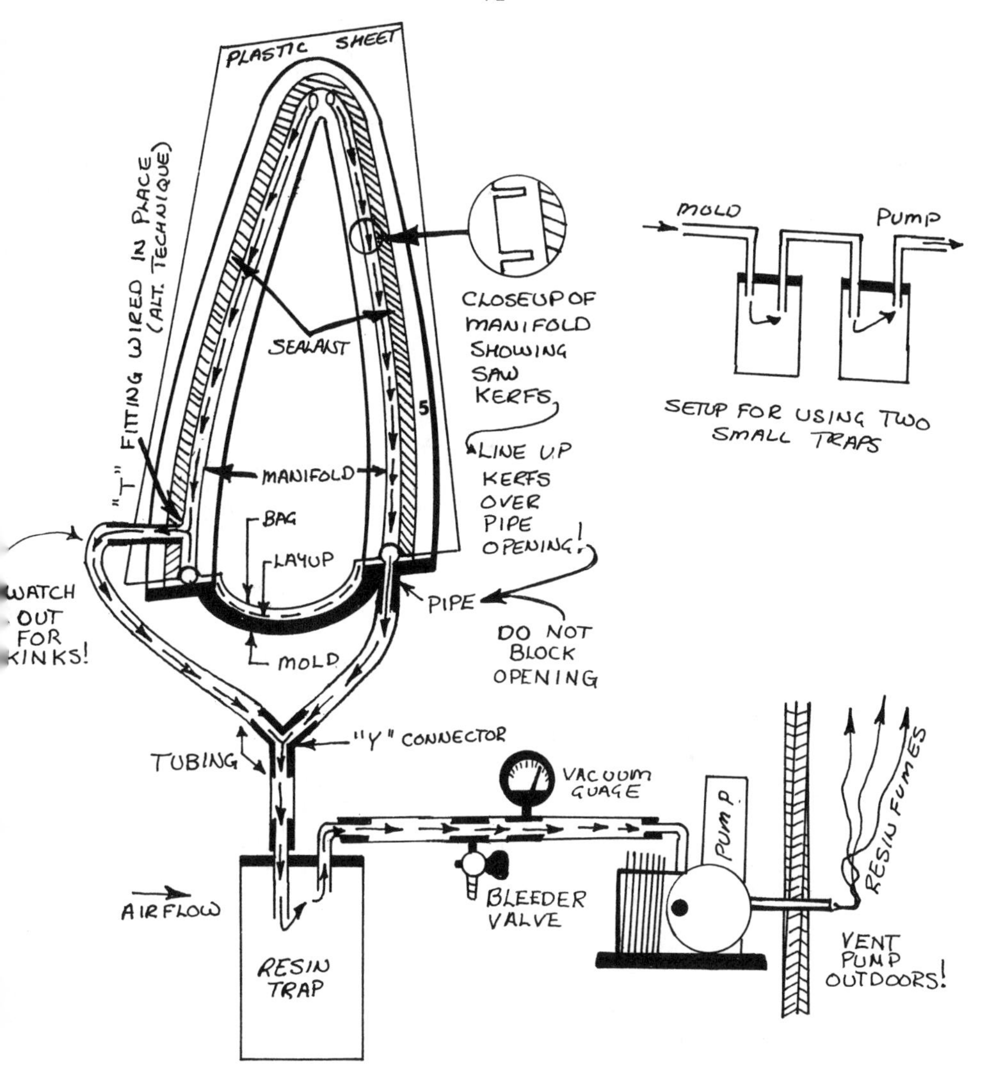

VACUUM MOLDING SETUP:
Drawing by Walbridge from Steve Rock notes

down so that the resin drains directly into the traps. If it were to collect in the loops and harden, the vacuum tubes would be blocked. Beware of kinks in the hose! The bleeder valve should be located on the line from the trap to the pump. The pump itself should be vented outside to remove resin fumes. Clark & Assoc. recommends keeping the pump in a sound insulated box. Its noises are not only annoying to the builders; they make locating air leaks almost impossible!

2. Wax the mold in the usual way, but DO NOT apply PVA. Seal shut all bolt holes in the mold flange by stuffing them with sealant and capping them with duct tape.

3. Apply sealant along the entire length of the waxed flange(at least 1¼" away from the inside edge and further if possible). Press the sealant in place with the backing paper still attached, the application should be checked for continuity. DO NOT remove the backing paper until the last minute, as resin and dirt may contaminate the sealant, crating a gap through which air can leak.

5. Apply PVA as before. With the setup work done, you're less likely to inadvertently damage the protective film.

6. Attach manifold approximately 3/4" away from the inside edge of the flange, bedding it in squares of sealant. If drain holes are used, be sure that they line up with drill holes or saw kerfs in the manifold so that the resin can drain out unimpeded.

   NOTE: It is recommended that the builder attempt a "dry run" prior to actual building to isolate leaks and deal with any problems peculiar to the individual setup. The sealant can be used for both the dry run and the final lamination. The cloth can be cut and put in place, and the mold sealed with the bag at this time.

   CAUTION: The need for cleaniless around the vacuum-bagging apparatus connot be overemphasized. A single piece of debris can puncture the bag, causing a catastrophic leak. Dirt,dust, or resin can contaminate the sealant, making it ineffective. The sealant backing provides some protection, and should be left in place until the last minute. Be sure to replace it after a dry run !

DECIDING HOW MUCH VACUUM TO USE:

The exact amount of vacuum used is not critical, and since higher levels promote better fabric wetout, they should be used when possible. Unfortunately, high vacuum levels can contribute to outgassing, the "boiling away" of the resin system caused by greatly lowered vapor pressures inside the bag. Outgassing is normally not a problem, since the bag is pressing down on it so that it is not in contact with the vacuum per se. But if the layup is squeegied or sucked so dry so that the cloth and not the resin supports the bag, the vacuum will appear between the fibers and outgassing can occur. The higher the vacuum, the worse the outgassing.

Outgassing can be enhanced by the following factors:

1. Too much squeegieing: This removes too much resin, allowing the bag to be supported by the fabric. The vacuum will infiltrate the resin and cause it to outgas.
2. Long gel times (90 minutes or more) permit too much resin to be removed and leaves too much time for outgassing afterwards.
3. Low viscosity resin makes it easy to squeegie out too much resin and permits the layup to be sucked dry.
4. Heated molds cause the resin viscosity to drop and increase the vapor pressure of the resin, causing it to outgas at a lower vacuum. Heat will, however, shorten the gel time.
5. Thin layups (less than 30 oz/sq yd or equivalent) will aggravate all these problems since such laminates can easily become resin starved.

In the absence of wide experience or extensive tests, the following guidelines are probably useful.

Vaccum Pressure	Type of Resin System
5"-10" Hg	Low Viscosity, Fast or slow gel, hea
5"-15" Hg	High Viscosity, Slow Gel, Heat
	Low Viscosity, Long gel

Vacuum Pressure:	Type of Resin System:
15-20" Hg	Low Viscosity, Fast Gel
15-25" Hg	High Viscosity, Slow Gel
20-30" Hg	High Viscosity, Fast Gel

These guidelines are given on the assumption that excessive resin is not removed manually. Porous laminates often result when low-viscosity resins (under 500 cps) are over-aggressively squeegied. It is unusual, however, to remove too much of a high viscosity (3000+ Cps) resin from a layup. It is important to have a feel for the layup as you work. Even thin laminates should feel a bit "mushy" before gelation - never hard. Thicker layups are softer and, if Kevlar is used, softer yet. Unfortunately, this subjective "feel" comes only with experience. Reasonable sensitivity and observation, however, will reduce the danger of a gross error.

When thin laminates are planned, stay to the low end of the vacuum range to reduce the chances of removing too much resin.

WET LAYUP VACUUM BAGGING:

Wet layup vacuum bagging involves producing a very fast, sloppy hand layup and reducing its irregularities through pressure. Because the resin is well-distributed before the bag is applied, it is a good technique for use with high viscosity resin systems and boats with deep convolutions and complex curves (such as wildwater boats and Lettman-style integral knee braces. There are also fewer problems with this procedure when ribs and keels must be bagged in place. Start by putting down a thick layer of resin (DO NOT let it gel) followed by the fabric you plan to use in the laminate. Where the resin does not soak through, more should be added. Just don't use more than you would in a normal hand layup. Remove all wrinkles; air bubbles will come out after the bag is applied, so let them be. Trim the cloth so that it barely covers spring manifolds or barely touches plastic pipe manifolds. Be careful not to contaminate the sealant with resin. Check the laminate for any dirt or debris which could puncture the bag before moving on.

WORK QUICKLY !! The system is headed towards the gel point at each moment. This is no place for inexperienced builders.

ATTACHING THE "BAG"

This is one step where you are going to need help. The plastic sheet which makes up the "bag" must be 1' wider than the circumferance of the deck and hull, and two feet longer than the mold. (3' longer for wildwater boats).

Fold the sheet in half lengthwise, and with the help of your partner, line up the ends. Drop the sheet into the midline of the mold, being careful not to get resin on the edges of the bag (the sealant will not stick to resin-covered plastic). Starting at the center, place the sheet across the layup. Strip the backing off the sealant and press the edge of the sheet against it. Do not permit the plastic to "bridge" a gap; you must leave sufficient "bag" to follow all mold contours.

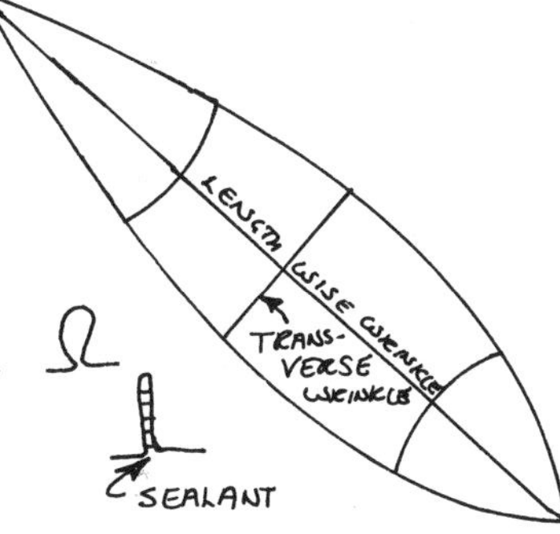

Athough the "bag material" is fairly flexible, it will not conform to the contours of the mold by itself. Wrinkles will develop, and these must be consolidated into several large ones which can be more easily managed. Three transverse wrinkles and one lengthwise wrinkle is usually needed; extra transverse wrinkles are useful when working on deep hulls and complex decks. See the illustration on the previous page for details.

These wrinkles are usually between 1" and 2" in height, but can be 12" or more. Where a wrinkle crosses the flange, it must be packed with seam sealer.to avoid leaks. Use whatever wrinkles are needed to avoid bridging; many small wrinkles are more complex, but still O.K.

When the bag has been set as well as possible, press it down firmly on the sealant and turn the pump on. Adjust the vacuum with the bleeder valve to less than 1" Hg, so that the bag can still be moved around. Remove as many wrinkles as possible by consolidating small wrinkles into larger ones. Be sure that the bag is not bridging over any deep convolutions. The lengthwise wrinkle can be pulled out of the center of slalom boat hulls, where bridging is impossible, but it should be left at the ends and in decks. Close the bleeder valve completely and seal up the leaks, which should now be hissing unless they are quite large. The layup is now ready to be squeegied.

SQUEEGIEING:

The first goal is to work out all pockets of air; the biggest ones first. This is done by pushing them with the surrounding resin; however, it is most important that most of the effort be directed towards removing air rather than resin. Once the layup is almost air-free, if excess resin remains, it can be removed; however, most of the excess is gotten rid of while working on the air. Since air usually concentrates in sharp concavities, work on these areas first. It is wise to leave more resin here than in the more accessible spots.

Air will appear as small circular light spots, ranging in size from a pinhead to an inch or more in diameter. Sometimes, as in the case of bag leaks, they are interconnected. It is most easily spotted in unpigmented resins; heavy pigment (white is the worst !) and Kevlar laminates are more difficult . It helps to work under a bright light, since air between the bag and the layup can be seen when light is reflected off the bag. This air is a sure indication of more air in the layers below.

Start slightly to one side of the center of the deck or hull and work across to the sides. Flex the squeegie slightly so that the corners will not dig in too deeply, allowing even pressure to be applied to the layup. You can apply considerable force if the resin is thick and the laminate is heavy, but be careful not to overdo. If a white spot appears, you're moving too much resin. If you start to wrinkle the cloth, back off. With thin layups and low-viscosity resins,much less force is needed. If there is unsaturated cloth at the edges, move resin next to the dry areas, but not into them. Vacuum pressure and capillary action will do the rest without the risk of trapping air. Excessive pressure on the squeegie can move reinforcing pieces or even puncture the bag; but an intelligent worker can easily tell when to ease off.

Once the resin is distributed and the air removed, you can begin to remove any excess. Pull the resin across the edge of the mold all the way to the flange, where the vacuum can carry it away. Bear in mind that it is easy to remove too much resin. The layup should feel slightly soft, so that if you press down with your thumb, an impression will remain. Leave extra in the bow and stern, and at any depressions in the mold where bubbles might collect.

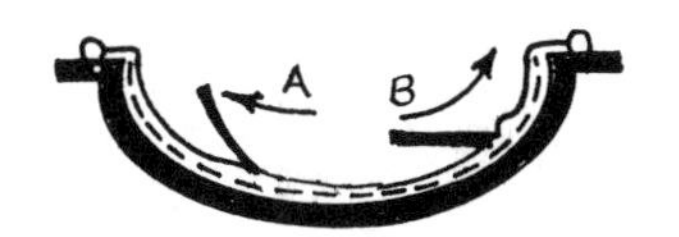

Two common squeegieing techniques: A is best suited to low-viscosity resins and heated molds; B is more powerful, and works best with high viscosity resin systems. In using "B", take care not to overdo and puncture the bag.

Complex undulations or peaks in the mold require extra attention. Be certain that there is enough bag to cover them when you lay the boat up. Valleys may harbor long, thin air bubbles which require coordinated effort to move. Use your fingers instead of a squeegie. If this does not work, try flooding out the area by moving excess resin into the voids.

Fabric bridging is an equally serious problem. The fabric itself can bridge across a keel area or around the cockpit and because the laminate is often opaque, the problem can be very difficult to detect. Once vacuum has been applied these bridged areas become very firm and solid and are almost impossible to work out. One must be very suspicious of sharp concavities where this is prone to happen, and see that the fabric lies flat against the mold before the full pressure of the bag comes down on it.

CAUTION: Excessive squeegie work around bridged areas can puncture the bag.

Wrinkles pose special problems. As a squeegie approaches a wrinkle, the resin preceding the squeegie will tend to follow the wrinkle rather than move in the direction of the squeegie. If this is a problem, let resin build under the wrinkle then follow it up to the flange. It's best to leave the folds resin-rich, since air bubbles tend to accumulate here and can do considerable damage to a resin-starved laminate.

WARNING: Bag pressure must be maintained until the part has cured. If it fails, the laminate will "spring back" to regular hand layup thickness, absorbing considerable air in the process and ruining the part. This is why such stress is placed on maintaining the vacuum.

DRY LAYUP VACUUM BAGGING:

Dry vacuum-bag layups tend to trap less air, are faster (allowing the use of hotter systems), and are cleaner and neater (which means less contact with toxic materials). The bag can also be sealed when the cloth is dry, permitting leaks to be located and plugged without worrying about the gel time of the system. In essence, the "test run" is a part of the process, eliminating considerable hassle with the bag. However, the amount of resin needed must be carefully figured out in advance. The best way to do this is to separate the "fiberglass" and "synthetic" fabrics and weigh them individually. Fiberglass will absorb about a half its weight in resins; synthetics need about their own weight. Multiply by 1.3 for hulls and 1.4-1.5 for convoluted decks and wildwater-type hulls. This leaves some extra resin which will be bled out: an experienced fabricator can cut these quantities by 10%

Place the cloth in the mold without any resin. If any reinforcements tend to slip out of place, they can quickly be basted to the cloth below with needle and thread. Seal the bag over the mold, evacuate it, and seal the inevitable leaks. A relatively high vacuum (as much as your pump will pull) is helpful in isolating any leaks. When all is in readiness, open up the bleeder valve so the bag can be moved (or turn the pump off) and remove the bag for several inches at each end. Pour HALF of the predetermined amount of resin UNDERNEATH THE CLOTH at each end, then reseal the bag. For best results, two people should work at opposite ends and pour together. The resin will start to run towards the center of the boat; it is important to distribute it across the full length of the boat, so that subsequent squeegieing is crosswise, towards the flanges. If extra people are available, have them retain some of the resin at the bow and stern by pressing on the bag with their hands, blocking the flow. Eliminate gross wrinkles so that the cloth in the laminate lies flat against the mold, then close the bleeder valve down until the desired vacuum is reached.

SQUEEGIEING:

Squeegieing technique is much the same with both wet and dry vacuum bagged layups; a few differences, however, are worthy of note. The vacuum will do a pretty good job of wetting out the cloth; the purpose of squeegieing is not to wet the cloth faster, but to bring extra resin to the advancing "front" to supply further saturation. NEVER push resin into an unsaturated area; air will become mixed with it and be very difficult to remove. Squeegie from the bottom of the mold (where most of the resin is) to remove any air which may have become trapped when the resin was poured. Poorly saturated areas will often appear milky. If you suspect that there is not enough resin in a given part of a layup, try to move the excess to it from other areas as soon as possible. When most of the fabric is saturated there is little free resin left, redistributing the rest is very difficult. Finish by removing surplus resin as with a wet layup, bearing in mind that all the cautions about over squeegieing apply here.

DETECTING LEAKS IN THE SYSTEM:

This applies to both wet and dry vacuum bag setups

A leak in the vacuum bag, however small, can be disasterous if not plugged quickly. All precautions must be taken to minimize leaks, to plug them quickly, and to keep leaked-in air from spreading if the source of the problem can't be found immediately. The need for cleanliness in the shop cannot be overstressed, as many leaks are caused by dirt and debris.

Large leaks are quite apparent, and can be isolated by ear. Run along the flange to track down the source of any whistling sounds, paying close attention to folds, intakes, and other problem areas. Smaller leaks may go unnoticed, but the air entering the layup will be apparent. Usually it appears as a rootlike pattern of small, interconnecting light spots which either spread in all directions or travel along reinforcements, bag wrinkles, mold depressions, or other low pressure areas. Large leaks can be spotted and plugged with bits of sealant which should be kept handy for this purpose. Smaller ones are harder to isolate, but the aerated areas can be surrounded by a circular ridge of resin. This will keep the bag from touching the fabric and prevent more air from entering. Work up a second concentric circle of resin outside the first. The resin outside these ridges should be void-free. If air appears between the ridges, the leak has been passed. If an isolated spot of air appears at the center of a widening pattern, the leak can be plugged. If not, squeegie as much resin as possible into the suspected area and leave it. After the layup has been squeegied to satisfaction, check the layup for small leaks which may have gone undetected.

Leaks can be sealed with wide strips of transparent tape. Don't use duct tape; you need to be able to see whether you've done the job.

TROUBLESHOOTING:

Abstracted from Advanced Fabrication Techniques for Whitewater Boats by W.A. Clark and Associates. Used by permission. We highly recommend this excellent publication to anyone planning to "Bag".

PROBLEM: No vacuum or weak vacuum at the start of the procedure.

POSSIBLE SOLUTIONS:

1. Small leaks along the flanges; minor breaks in the bag.
2. Stuck bleeder valve; reversed, leaky, or broken vacuum gauge.
3. Connection to the exhaust side of the pump; improper connection of pump to traps to mold; leaky connections anywhere.
4. Kinked, broken, or collapsed tubing. Heavy objects on hoses. Hoses caught in door. Cured resin in hoses.
5. Leaky resin traps; traps improperly sealed; broken or out-of-place gaskets.
6. Bleeder hole in flange blocked with cured resin; bleeder hole blocked by manifold (hole in manifold must overlie vent hole)
7. Sealant unusable; loss of tack due to dust or resin contamination; cloth yarns extending over sealant, preventing a complete seal

PROBLEM: Sudden loss of vacuum during procedure.

Must be diagnosed without delay, as it will lead to expansion of the laminate as pressure is relieved, infiltration of the laminate by air and, unless there is time to re-bag the part (adding extra resin to do this), the layup is ruined.

1. Resin traps or plumbing filled with resin. Many resins "foam" when allowed to set up in large quantities. The traps must be large enough to contain it !
2. Resin trap failure due to cracking (glass traps), implosion due to vacuum pressure; expansion due to heat of curing resin plugs. Use adequate traps, and have spares handy.
3. Vacuum pump failure, usually due to running a mold-heating apperatus and a pump on the same circuit, or by connecting the pump with questionable wiring.
4. Boiling formulation, rare, except when excessive vacuum is used, or during experimental layups.
5. Bag leaks or ruptures due to a)embrittled, dried out bag b) bag bridging c)sharp debris on inside of bag d) weakened bag caused by wetting due to sweat, condensation, etc. e) sharp edges on manifold/bleeders f) overagressive squeegieing g)sharp fingernails, jewelry, etc.

6) Bag sealant fails, allowing the bag to shear inward, causing a leak. Repair with additional sealant. Non-specialized sealants (caulking) will have to be watched especially closely.

ACHIEVING A CURE:

CONTROL OF TEMPERATURE is the key to a reliable cure. Most systems cure at "room temperature"; ie between 60 and 90 degrees. For a "low heat cure" the temperature is raised between 90 and 150 degrees. Anything more requires specialized equipment; ie: a boat oven, and falls under the heading of a high-heat cure.

POLYESTER RESIN SYSTEMS are generally cured at room temperature for 24-48 hours. If the temperature is too low (under 60 degrees) the cure will take months unless special promoters are used. Excessive heat (over 120 degrees) can warp the layup and (in the case of molds made with polyester resin) the mold as well.

VINYLESTERS can be promoted for both room temperature and heat cures. Although the former is more popular, heat cures give better control over gel and cure time, and are thus preferred by commercial users. They work until done, then switch on the heat for a fast cure. Since the resin will take months to set up at room temperature, there's never a worry about pot life.

EPOXIES have various curing requirements, depending on the system. The polyamids used by boatbuilders cure at room temperature; many of the more exotic systems require a heat cure. In some cases, a low heat cure followed by a high heat cure gives the best results. The supurb boats produced by the great builders of the 70's: Clark, Rock, Brown, Wright, Waddell, and McKnight all utilized heat-cured epoxies. Because of the superiority of their materials, their boats have not been equalled to this day.

SUN CURES:

You can accelerate the cure times of many resin systems by leaving the layup in the sun on a clear, warm day. One caution: if the boat is put in the sun too early when building with one of the "esters", the heat of the sun will combine with the heat of the reaction to cause warping. To be safe, allow the resin to set up solidly (firm enough to trim), then put it in the sun. Stay out of direct sunlight during lamination; the "light" parts will set up while the shaded parts remain liquid, causing problems.

Bill McKnight has a different kind of "sun cure" which acts as an alternative to an oven. The boat should first be cured, popped, seamed, and outfitted with walls so it will maintain its shape. Wrap your boat in black plastic, tape securely closed, and set on cradles (to prevent deformation) in the sun. The inside temps will reach 150-160 degrees, giving many of the benefits of a heat cure.

MOLD HEATERS:

The foregoing material is abstracted from Advanced Fabrication Techniques for Whitewater Boats by Clark Associates, Boulder, Colorado. Used with permission of the author.

Resistance heaters capable of warming a mold to 100°C (212°F) may be woven into a layer of cloth and incorporated into the mold during construction. They may also be bag molded or, with great difficulty, contact molded to the back of existing molds. In either case, be sure that the HDT of the mold is adequate, and that precautions are taken against fire and shock hazzards.

Begin by cutting a layer of coarse fabric (i.e: 18 Oz. woven roving about 6" longer and wider than the proposed mold dimensions includ ing the width of the flange. Taking care to see that the fabric is not distorted in handling, draw a line to show where the outer edge of the flange will be. The heater elements cannot extend beyond the flange. Bind the edges of the fabric with masking tape to prevent unravelling and transfer the cloth to a flat, clean work area.

To determine how much power the heater will draw, you'll have to estimate the surface area of the mold. One way to do this is to cut fabric of a known weight per square yard to the appropriate shape and weigh it. Clark Associates recommends loads of 200 watts per sq. ft. for Vinylester, 300 watts per sq. ft. for Epoxy. To handle this, John Brown recommends using one strand of 24-30 guage copper transformer wire every two rovings; on 18 oz. material this means ½" spacing. Although bare wire can be used, Clark recommends Teflon or polyamide insulation effective to 180°C. Use 30 guage wire for temperatures up to 200°F; 24 guage if higher temperatures will be required.

Two weave patterns are shown below. The redundand weave permits added temperature control as well as a backup in case of heater failure. Temperature is controlled with a variac, which most of us have used as a household light dimmer. In a dual system, two variacs are required.

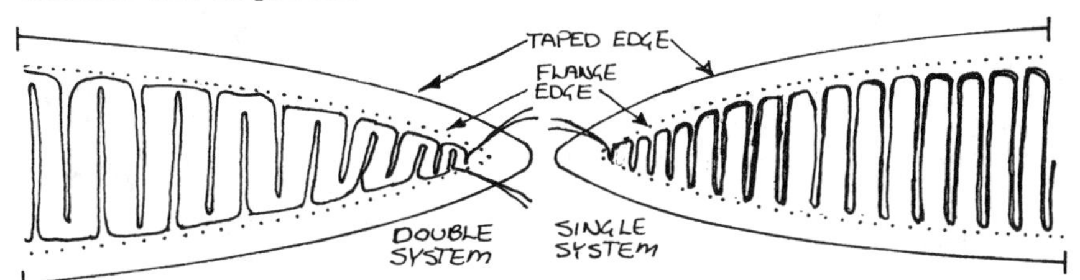

CAUTION: BE CERTAIN that your wiring is up to handling these loads before proceding. 1000 watts is close to the limit of many household systems. If you aren't sure, ask an electrician. One builder I know burned down his house with a mold heater.

Weave the wire into the roving with a double strand of wire, going over and under several roving strands at a time. At the end of each "heater", solder several feet of type AF asbestos fixture wire using non-corrosive flux. If the heater is not the last layer of the mold, this "pigtail" will need to be pulled through subsequent layers and kept in a plastic bag to protect it from resin contamination. You can pull it free of the vacuum bagging process and use it to help cure the mold.

The finished mold should be backed with 2-3" of urethane foam insulation to minimize heat loss from the bottom of the mold and maximize efficiency. Terminate the "pigtail" in a plug for safety and convenience.

People who don't have access to heated molds can get similar results by attaching pipe heat tapes (used to keep plumbing from freezing) to the back of a mold. A few cautions. First, know the HDT of your mold and don't do this without asking the mold owner Second, do not cross wires or add insulation, as this could cause a fire. Heat tapes can be used to help cure seats and seams where needed.

Heated molds are a hassle, but they have a number of advantages. Because you can control temperature precisely, you can warm a mold in a cold shop, heat resin for improved handling qualities, and provide controlled, reliable cures. Heat can cause some problems including 1) embrittlement of the PVA sheet (use Kapran); 2) gassification of the resin under vacuum pressure (use less pressure) decreased gel and cure times (start work at low heat (80-90°F) and go higher only when ready to start the final cure.

OVENS: CONSTRUCTION AND USE:

Boaters wishing to avoid the problems of heated molds or who wish to cure at temperatures beyond the HDT of their mold's material will need to construct an oven large enough to accomodate a boat. The major problem is size: an oven large enough to accomodate a wildwater C-2 (or even a slalom kayak) is going to take up the better part of somebody's garage.

CAUTION: Beware electrical overloads. Someone I know burned his house down because of poor planning in this area. Have your wiring checked before you set up the oven!

OVENS can be constructed with a minimum of engineering knowledge. You need an air-tight, well-insulated fireproof box of the proper size, an electric heater/ blower combination, and slings to suspend the boat. The heater should be shielded to keep it from heating the boat directly by radiation. Temperature can be controlled via a thermostat, or by monitoring several thermometers placed at intervals throughout the oven and adjusting a variac. The blower motor should be outside the unit if possible so that it will not overheat.

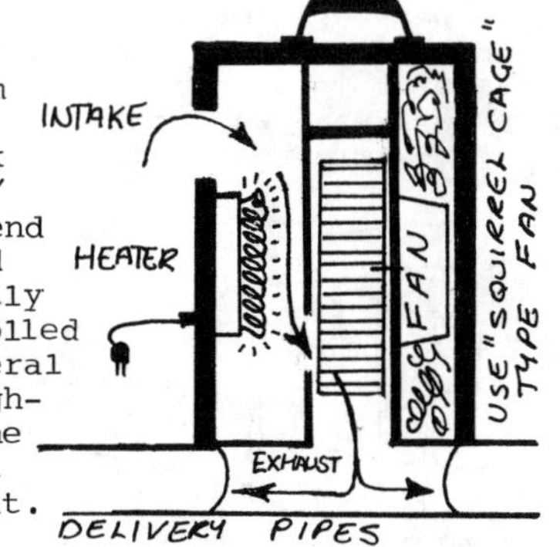

In Chicago and Madison a site for a permanent oven could not be found, so an effective, portable substitute was constructed. An old C-2 mold (A large crate or a framework covered with a tarp would do equally well) was procured and filled with vermiculite. The boat was set inside, and more vermiculite poured in along the sides. About 4"-6" of fiberglass insulation was put on top of the boat. The heating unit (diagramed above) consisted of a five gallon can containing two 500 watt cone heaters and a blower, with two 4'x3" pipes extending from it, and several intake holes. The exhaust opening empties into two pipes, which are extended into the ends of the boat to distribute the heat.

When all is in readiness, lower this unit inside. The air intake should be placed so as to take in air from the inside of the boat. Chink around the cockpit for a tight seal. When the unit is in place and covered with insulation, monitor the temperature by means of thermometers thrust into the vermiculite and adjust by means of a variac. Ambient air from outside should be piped into the area around the motor, which will overheat otherwise. Warping of the boat being cured is unlikely, even if the HDT is exceeded, since the boat is supported almost perfectly by the vermiculite. All meltables such as ethafoam should be removed beforehand. Synthetic fabrics (nylon, polypropylene) should be heat cured before being used in the layup. Hollow ribs should have a hole drilled in them so that the expanding air will not force them to "pop" loose.

TRIMMING:

Trimming involves cutting the laminate flush with the edge of the mold. It is an essentially very simple job which can be made almost impossible through lack of attention to detail. It is also quite easy to damage the mold during this procedure. So pay close attention.

TIMING is critical. As the resin hardens, the boat becomes increasingly difficult to trim. The secret of hassle-free trimming is to work on the laminate as early in the cure cycle as you can. What makes this job challenging is that each material has its own "earliest possible" cutting point, and that the resin is continuing to harden all the time and won't stay the same for long. As a result, most builders will find it necessary to "babysit" their boats during the cure.

FIBERGLASS can be cut effectively when the resin has just gelled. NYLON, CAP, and POLYPROPYLENE need the resin to be fully gelled, and just starting to become hard. KEVLAR cannot be cut until the resin is quite hard, close to the end of the cure cycle. With this in mind, there are several possible techniques:

1) Wait until the most reluctant layer is ready to be cut, then cut the entire laminate. This technique works quite quite well for thin laminations of conventional materials, and with difficulty if there is one layer of Kevlar. With more than five layers or two layers of Kevlar, you can expect a good bit of trouble. BEWARE of cutting too early. A not-uncommon problem is for the fiberglass and nylon to cooperate, but for the Kevlar to resist. The builder, in his efforts to cut the Kevlar, tears apart the laminate along the edge. This causes considerable damage which is almost impossible to repair.

2) Wait for each layer to set up to optimum as you build, and trim each layer before proceding further. Unless you want to stay up all night, though, you'll need a system with a very predictable cure time and plenty of patience. This technique is used by John R. Sweet in building his boats.

Many people use step 1, but make the following efforts during construction to minimize difficulties in trimming. Kevlar patterns can be cut slightly undersized so that the layer ends just below the edge of the mold. This takes a good set of patterns! Even if this is not possible, patch pieces can be cut so that they don't overlap the flange, minimizing the buildup of thickness there. Be careful: you need full thickness along the seam line to assure good seams!

The proper tool for in-the-mold trimming is a very sharp knife. A hooked linolium knife works well, as does a high-quality, well sharpened paring knife. A razor knife with replaceable blades is a good second choice for those not handy with a sharpening stone. Don't use a hunting knife or any other knife with a thick back. Wear leather work gloves for protection against slips, and position your hands so they'll be out of the way if the knife should slip. Keep the blade sharp; a dull knife needs to be pulled harder, and this increases the chances of injury.

TECHNIQUE: Work from the inside of the mold out; the knife will press the boat against the flange and make the job easier. At times you may have to work from the outside in, but be aware that the boat can be pushed away from the hull, making it easy to cut below the seam line. Be very careful not to scratch the mold or flange, or to cut into any alignment projections which may stick out from the latter. Most of the difficulty in trimming occurrs at the ends, especially in low-volume boats. It is very easy to get below the seam line, particularly if the angle of the flanges is unfavorable. Work outside the mold if you have doubts.

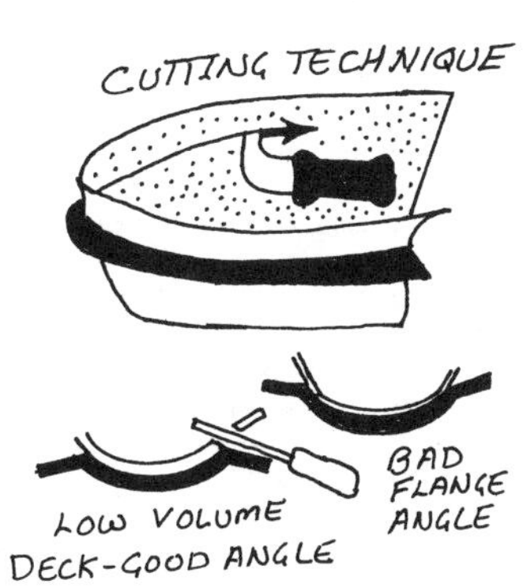

IF THE LAMINATE IS TOO TOUGH FOR A KNIFE, you'll have to resort to other measures. The problem often results when you don't have time to "babysit" a laminate through curing; when curing is unexpectedly slow, or in vacuum-bagging, when the laminate is simply not accessible. The boat will have to be removed from the mold, and the laminate trimmed with a sabre saw or hacksaw.

CAUTION: NEVER use a saw of any kind inside a mold. No matter how good you think you are, the risks of a single slip are too severe. One of the finest boatbuilders I know savaged a C-2 mold because of a moment's carelessness. Even if you don't make major errors, its easy to scratch the flange badly with a saw when trying to cut the laminate flush.

Once the boat is free of the mold, the seam line will be clearly visible. Cut slowly, making the line as smooth and straight as possible. Haste will result in a wavy line and this will complicate the seaming job later. The process will consume many sabre saw blades, so have extras on hand. Wear a respirator and use eye protection. Gross irregularities in the seam line can be removes with a Sureform File, but this is, at best, a slow process.

SEAMING:

The weakest part of any white water boat is the seam line, where the deck and hull meet. With careful attention, though, you can make it the strongest part. Seam strength is particularly important to heavy-water surfers, pop-up and ender artists, big hole riders, and other assorted hot dogs.This is also the part most frequently under-engineered by builders of commercial boats.

PREPARATION along the seam line is important. If your timing is good and the inner layer remains tacky, you can procede directly to allignment and seaming. Few of us will be so lucky; most end up grinding the hull for 3" on either side of the seam line down to the underlying fibers to insure that the seam will bond. An alternative used by many fabricators is to lay a peel-ply fabric (special materials are available, but polypro, nylon, and CAP work fine) along the edges of the seam. Use 4" wide tape, laid in place when the lamination is done. When pulled free after the cure, peel-ply leaves a rough surface behind which will be ready for seaming with only light sanding.

ALIGNMENT: Bringing the deck and hull together so that their edges line up is easy with a good flanged mold: after trimming, just bolt it together and start seaming. The cockpit hole provides access to the interior.

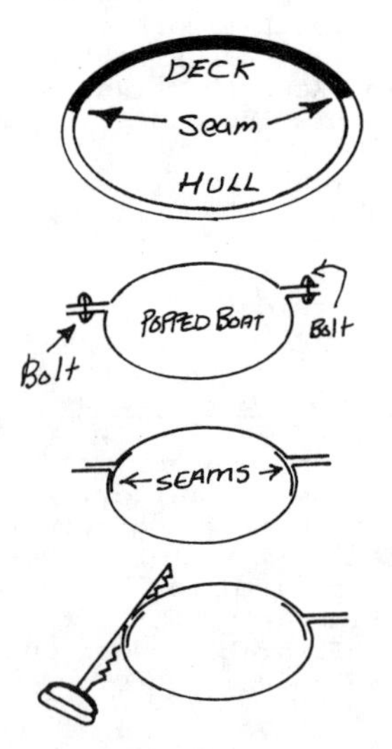

Vacuum bag molds and some others may lack cockpit holes, so you'll need to cut one. Clark recommends aligning the two halves by popping the boats, then clamping the two halves together using the cloth which overlaps the flange. The problem is removing this mess after seaming, especially without the $200 "pneumatic milling cutter" Clark recomends. Unless you like grinding, try the "warped or flanged mold" technique listed below.

WARPED OR UNFLANGED MOLDS cannot be bolted together to get good alignment, and require a different approach. The following technique, which requires a roll or two of 1" masking tape and a lot of patience, allows you to seam outside the mold. You'll also need a knife or hacksaw blade to help line up the edges.

1. Pop the boat (see the next section).
2. Place the deck on top of the hull, bow to bow and stern to stern.
3. Line up the bow and stern and tape them firmly together. This part of the boat is pretty rigid, so alignment isn't usually a problem. Tape firmly together.
4. Line up the edges as follows: a) stick a knife or hacksaw blade betweeen the edges, and pry the two halves into approximate alignment. Do this for the first 2-4 feet on one end, one side at a time. b) now go over the seam again, making the edges line up perfectly. c) press the edges firmly together and tape them in place. Then move up the seam further and repeat the process. The first part of this procedure uses very little tape, but by the time you are through, the entire seam will be covered with overlapping lengths of tape.
5. Handle the taped boat with GREAT CARE, as rough treatment may "spring" the edges, making it necessary to redo long sections of seam.

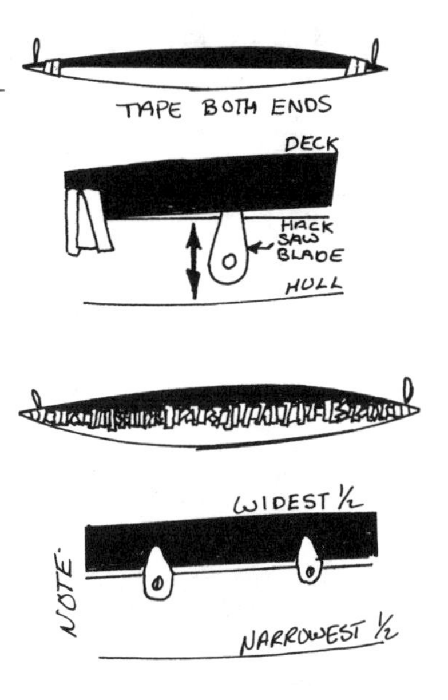

NOTE: Once a boat is popped, it should be seamed at once. If the two halves are stored separately, they will warp and make normal alignment techniques marginally effective. If this happens to you, attach tabs of sheet metal to the outside of the narrowest piece with sheet metal screws. The tabs cradle the other half of the boat, making taping easier. In extreme cases, you can put in a second screw and join the two halves together. Afterwards, back out the screws and cover the hole with an outside seam.

After alignment, the two halves are joined together with overlapping layers of fiberglass tape laid along the seam line inside and (sometimes) out. Laying the tape on the inside is a messy, repulsive job, but one which, if done wrong, can make owning a home-made boat a real hassle. The best way to tell what kind of a craftsman built your boat is to look at the inside seam.

MANUFACTURED SEAM TAPES are readily available in 7.5 oz E-Glass in any width from 1" on up. Since this material is substantially weaker than those used in laying up the hull and deck (especially if you use S-Glass or Kevlar) the experienced homebuilder will be better off cutting strips from scraps of cloth. The disadvantage of such strips (aside from the tedium of cutting them) is that the edges are unfinished. Unless you are very neat and careful, the loose fibers along the edges and tangle, causing serious problems. DO NOT cut the tape along the finished edge of the cloth; it is impossible to get this "half-finished" tape to track along the seam line and lie down properly. Take the time to get the edges even, and to remove loose strands.

Here are a few common layup patterns. Racing boats use two layers, cruising boats need three to four. We recommend an outside seam on either. Note how the layers overlap to avoid sudden changes in flexibility which create stress risers in the hull. The innermost layer should be a synthetic, like Nylon or Kevlar. The other layers should be fiberglass.

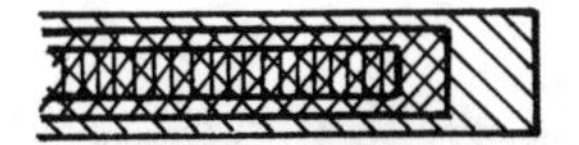

1) OVERLAPPING TAPES: 1½", 2", and 3" fiberglass/nylon

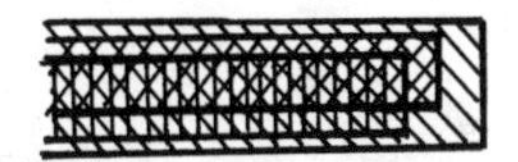

2) OFFSET 2" TAPE covered with 3" synthetic.

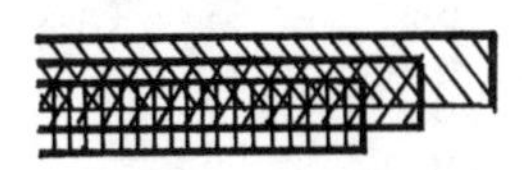

3) THREE LAYER OFFSET 2" tape, all fiberglass.

TO SEAM WITH LEAST EFFORT, set the boat on edge at shoulder height or slightly less using slings or dollies. If the mold is suitably framed, a table is ideal. BE SURE to cover your hair with a bag or bathing cap; resin will give it a permanent wave that has to be cut out. Wear a respirator. A vacuum cleaner, set with the intake inside the boat, will improve air circulation.

SEAM ROLLING TECHNIQUE:

1) Cut strips as long as the seam, minus 2" If you want to do each end separately, cut strips half as long as the seam. There will be a 4" overlap at center if you do this.
2) Lay out the seam as it will be placed in the boat on a clean bench. Sew the individual strips of cloth together using a wide basting stitch. This will keep them lined up during the next steps. If you are using a one-piece seam, mark the center on the tape and on the seam inside the boat.
3) Saturate the tapes with resin. You can do this by laying them on wax paper and using a brush, but it's easier to roll them loosely and dip them into a soup can filled with resin. If you do the latter, leave plenty of time for complete satuation.

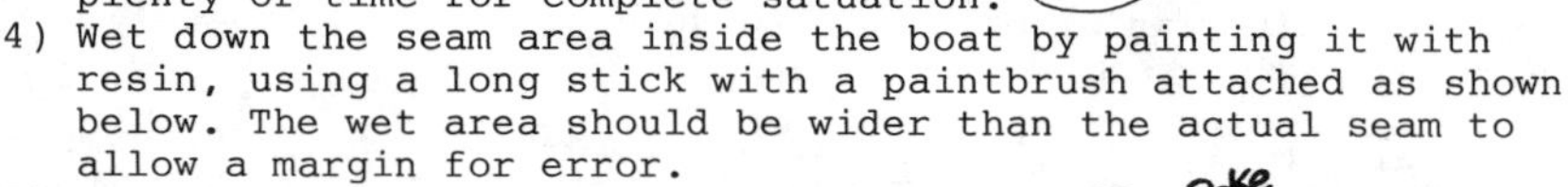

4) Wet down the seam area inside the boat by painting it with resin, using a long stick with a paintbrush attached as shown below. The wet area should be wider than the actual seam to allow a margin for error.
5) Roll the saturated seam material as shown. Place the scroll on the inside of the seam, lining up the center marks. Roll each end out to the bow or stern,pushing with the blunt end of the paitbrush-stick. Keep the scroll "on line"; if it veers to one side, push it on the other end to get it back on track.
6) CAUTION: Although excess tape may be forced into the end of your boat, it can seal off an air bubble in the tip making it impossible to get a solid end pour. This is why we cut the seams a bit short; the end plug will close the gap.
7) Go over the tape with a paintbrush to lay it flat andremove air bubbles. A contoured piece of Ethafoam on the end of the stick also works well. If the edges curl up, you've stretched the center of the tape. Pull back on the center and the edges will lie down.

This technique has two drawbacks:

1) It does not work well in low-volume boats, where the seam is in the bottom of a deep "Vee" and where end space is limited.
2) It does not work well with "home-cut" tapes; IE: tape cut from cloth. Paddlers are advised to use manufactured tapes for this procedure.

POINTED STICK TECHNIQUE:

This technique is simpler, and is used by many builders, including John Sweet and myself.

The tool that you will use is pointed stick, which can take several forms: the basic sharp stick; a stick with a nail on the end, angled to produce a "twist to release" feature; and lastly, a plastic clothespin screwed to the end of the stick, with a line running back to the end. A pull on the line releases the cloth. (This idea courtesy Sandy Williams)

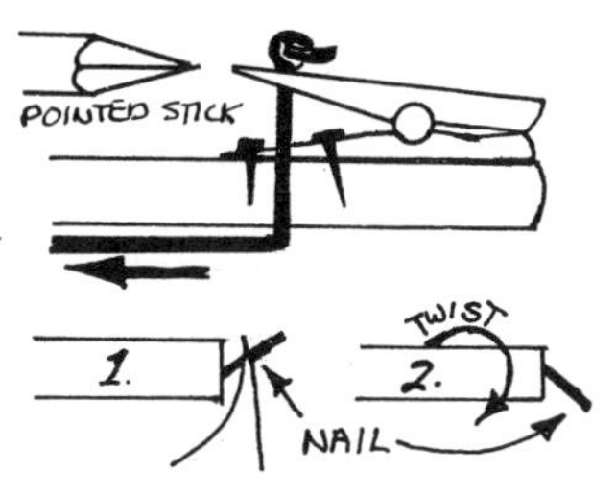

NOTE: With this procedure (and, to a lesser extent, with others) it is important to keep the stick clean. If you don't as the resin gels, the tool becomes sticky and releasing the seams at the proper time becomes extremely difficult. Wipe the stick off with solvent in between "pokes" for best results.

Here's how to do it:

1. Cut strips of tape half as long as the seam, less 1". John Sweet reports that he finds this length unwieldy, and prefers to cut this length into thirds. The "center third" is accessible directly from the cockpit, leaving the ends to be laid in.

2. Lay down a strip of wax paper with the seam tapes on top of it. Line them up the way you want them to lie in the boat, and saturate them fully. Some people will want to baste them together with cotton thread, but this is not necessary, as they will stay together quite well when resin-saturated.

3. Coat the seam area with resin. As before, the wet area should be an inch or so wider than the width of the overlapped tapes.

4. Put on your respirator and protective clothing.

5. Put the stick through one end of the length of seam tape, and take the other end in your hands. Drape the extra seam tape between your fingers so that it won't become twisted. Being careful not to drag the wet seam tape across the deck, extend the stick into one end of the boat. Let out the seam tape between your fingers as needed. Pin the stick end of the seam tape in the end of the boat, pull the intervening tape tight, and lower the rest of the seam into place. CAREFULLY release the end of the stick from the tape, and withdraw.

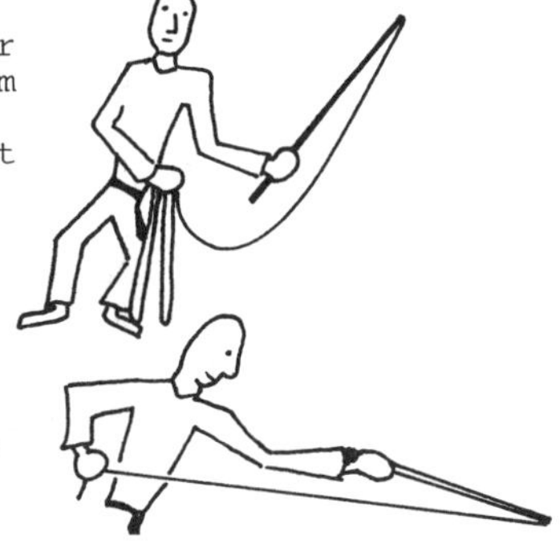

CAUTION: It is very easy to catch the stick on the seam tape as you remove it, pulling out your freshly-laid seam in the process. If this happens, curse loudly, then relax. Shove the point of the stick back into the bow and shake it back and forth. You can also peel the tape off the stick with a second, clean stick. If all else fails, remove the whole seam and try again. If only a few inches of seam tape has been disturbed when you pull back, it may be easier to push it back into place with the blunt end of the tool.

6. Once the seam is in place, run over it with a brush or freshly-cut piece of ethafoam soaked in resin to remove air bubbles. You can move the seam around or become tangled in loose ends, so don't overdo it.

7. Repeat the procedure for the other half of the seam (or, if working in thirds, the other end third).

THE GRAVITY TECHNIQUE:

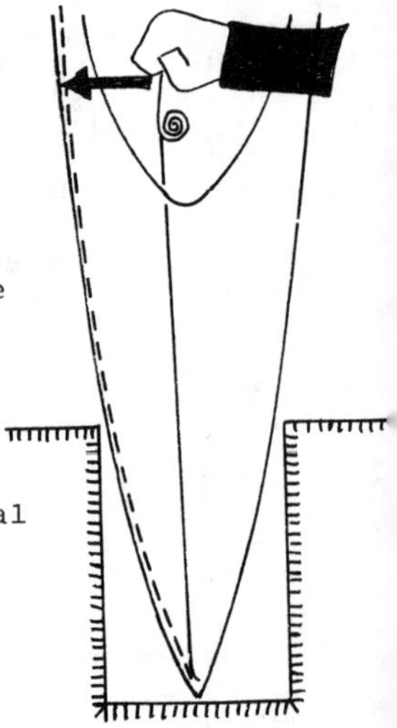

1. Place the boat nose first in a pit about 3' deep. This puts the cockpit at approx. shoulder height. If you don't have a pit handy, use a stepladder. The boat should be straight up and down and well secured.

2. Since you will be seaming both sides of the lower half of the kayak, prepare two 7' strip of tape for each layer you want to lay down. Paint the seam area with resin.

3. Saturate each layer of tape and roll it up. Bring one roll of tape into the cockpit, and allow it to unroll by gravitational action. With the lower end dangling about 1" above the tip of the kayak, slowly and carefully move your hand towards the seam, allowing the tape to settle centered over the seam along its length. (Several tries may be needed at first, but the procedure is relatively simple to learn)

4. Go over the entire length of the seam with a paintbrush or roller to remove air bubbles.

This technique comes courtesy of Brian Vanderploeg of the Cascade Kayak company, who cites two main advantages: 1) The styrene fumes collect at the bottom of the boat for safer, less smelly seaming and 2) the end pours form automatically from the runoff from the seams. I haven't tried it yet, but it sounds elegant !

ADDITIONAL HINTS:

1. It is very important to keep the seaming stick clean. If using an old stick, sand it smooth to remove fiberglass spicules and other potential snags. Wipe the ends with solvent to remove excess resin between layers, or keep a second clean stick in reserve. Watch where you put the stick down when not in use; it will pick up considerable dirt which will cause hassles inside the boat.

2. If something major goes wrong in seaming, pull out all the tape and start over. Don't waste valuable time fiddling; the resin is hardening all the time, and you may inadvertently disturb other layers of seam which are set properly. Remember: if a seam sets improperly, it'll take a hammer and chisel to set it right. A fresh seam will often go in with little trouble.

3) After seaming one side of the boat, let it gel thoroughly before turning the boat over and working on the other side. The resin should be hard, but may be still tacky. If you flip too early, the first seam could fall on your head while you apply the second.
4) To speed the cure on the inside, you can clamp two heat lamps to the cockpit rim and aim them towards the bow or stern. DO NOT aim directly at the boat or let the lamp come in contact with the laminate. Either could cause heat damage, or even start a fire. People using heat cured systems normally let the boat set up hard enough to pop, seam and outfit it, then use a high-temperature cure to bond everything together.
5) Polyester and vinylester users often try to save time when seaming by mixing up a very "hot mix". This is O.K. if you're very experienced, but leaves little margin for error. It also releases a greater than normal amount of obnoxious fumes which can burn the skin and eyes. I don't recommend the procedure no matter who likes it.
6) A narrow (2") roller attached to the end of a stick has been touted by a major British publication as being THE tool for seam work. You wind the cloth around the roller, then push it out. I haven't tried it, out of fear that the apparatus may be too bulky even in high volume boats.
7) Most builders light the inside of their boats by shining lights through the hull from the outside. This is not satisfactory when using opaque hulls, and lights clamped to the cockpit rim can get in the way. John Schriner uses a small TEKNA compact flash-light taped to the seam stick. It is unaffected by resin, can be cleaned with solvent, and is small enough to work even in low-volume boats.
8) Jesse Whittemore's preferred seam for squirt boats is a 1.5" bias-cut strip of Kevlar sandwiched between 1" and 2" fiber-glass tape. It is applied with the 1" tape down. It has several advantages. First, the 2" tape covers the ragged edge of the Kevlar, and second, the Kevlar stiffens the tapes making it fold easily to slip into narrow bows and sterns.

POPPING THE BOAT:

Once the seam has hardened (or when the laminate has hardened for outside-the-mold seaming), the time has come to remove the boat from the mold. If you have prepped the mold properly, this should be a very easy and satisfying step. But don't forget that impat-ience or carelessness can severely damage the mold. Do not hit the mold with a metal mallet or use metal tools inside the mold for any reason. The use of hammers of any kind (even rubber) is discouraged, as the impacts can crack the gelcoat on the inner surface of the mold. Following these rules will save you many hours of patching.

Follow this procedure:

1) Unbolt the mold completely. Be sure that all the bolts are out; it's easy to miss one then wonder why the flanges won't come apart.
2) Using a wood or Teflon wedge, pry the flanges apart. Do not use a screwdriver; it will scratch the flange. For seamed boats, this should be sufficient to pop the deck.
3) Using a long, thin Teflon wedge, pry the sides away from the mold. The idea is to get underneath the hull as well as the sides. This will usually give all the force needed for a good release.

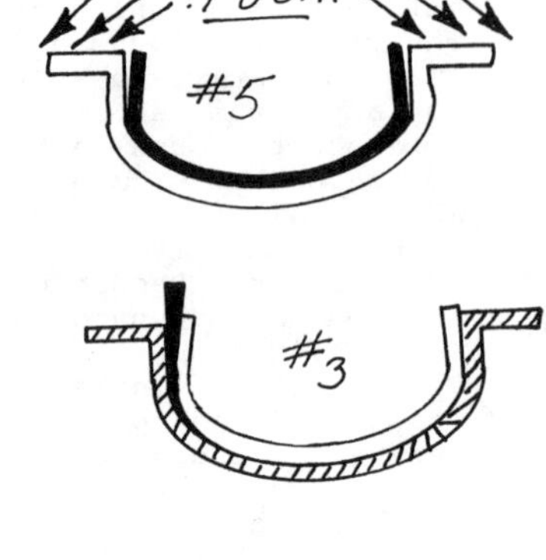

4) If you can't find a place to insert the wedge, you can "open up" the mold by applying <u>downward</u> and <u>outward</u> pressure to the flanges. Unless the mold is pretty flimsy, you won't do damage this way. But be alert for cracking sounds which might indicate the beginning of damage. (Figure 5)

5) If you still have difficulties, try working a length of thin nylon rope or flat nylon webbing under the bow or stern. With one person pulling at each end, you can force the line between the hull and the boat along its full length. Because tremendous, non-damaging force can be generated with this technique, it is especially useful with problem molds. Use the Teflon wedge to force the rope or webbing under the bow or stern.

6) For known problem releases or vacuum-bagged boats (the bows of wildwater boats are excellent candidates for this technique), leave a flap of cloth saturated with resin to harden over the flange. (2-3 layers should do it) By driving a wedge between the flange and the flap, you'll lift the boat out of the mold. The drawback is that this piece must be cut off afterwards, a surprisingly grubby job !

7) Years ago, boaters uses to release boats from molds by striking the mold with a rubber mallet. The mold flexes, releasing the boat. The problem is that this results in mold damage unless done with <u>utmost</u> care (AND NEVER, NEVER USE A METAL HAMMER !!!) A teflon wedge is so much better that smart builders leave the mallets in their tool boxes.

8) If you've tried all this and you're still stuck, you've got trouble !! The danger is that further efforts to remove the boat will damage the mold. I have peeled boats out of molds with known release problems (because of silicone contamination) with the above techniques without difficulty. At this point you should call the mold owner for suggestions.

9) One more idea which I've only heard of: sometimes it helps to force water between the boat and the mold to dissolve the PVA. Follow this by leaving the whole mess out of doors in freezing weather; the expanding ice will do the job.

Once you get over how NICE your boat looks, check the mold for damage. Since it is good form to return the mold clean and lightly waxed, you can do both the checking and cleaning together. Resin globs on the flange and elsewhere should be removed with a stiff, non-mettalic tool. Thin layers of resin adhering to the flange can be gently scraped off. If the boat has taken part of the mold with it, or if the surface is rough to the touch, consult the mold owner. Some will ask you to make repairs; some will want the mold returned "as is". For information on how to do this, check back to the "mold preparation" section.

AN OUTSIDE SEAM:

On many factory boats, the outside of the seam is either covered with tape or left bare. This is not good, since an outside seam strengthens the weakest part of the joint and adds considerable strength with very little extra weight. Racers should use a single layer fiberglass seam on the outside; cruisers will use a two-layer seam with fiberglass in, synthetic out.

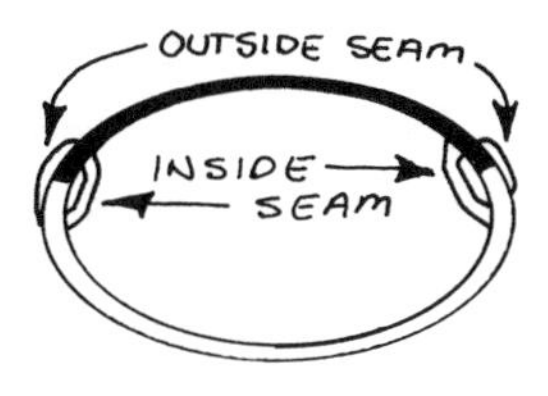

Here's how to do it:

1)Rough up the seam area so that a strip ¼"-½" wider than the tape is well-sanded. Several people have gotten good results by tapin a thin strip of peel-ply along the outside of the mold, which eliminates the need for sanding. Since excessive sanding will scratch the hull and do cosmetic damage, lay out guidelines with calipers or hand measurements before firing up your power tools.

2)Lay a line of fiberglass-reinforced strapping tape at either side of the proposed seam. Strapping tape is preferred to masking tape, since it does not tear apart as it is removed. Below this, cover the deck and hull with wax paper, Polyethylene sheet, or multiple layers of newspaper to catch resin dribbles. Set the boat on the opposite, unmasked edge.

3) Cut the appropriate lengths of 2" Glass Tape (1" Glass & 2" synthetic for 2-layer seams). Paint outside seam area with resin.

4) Roll out the tape along the seam line and saturate it. Try to catch large drips of resin. Trim the ends as needed. To neatly cover the bow and stern, extend the tape around the nose and trim as shown.

5) Take a polyethylene sheet (1½ mil preferred) and lay it over the seam. Pull it down tightly, and smooth out the wrinkles with your fingertips. If you break the film, apply a second layer and continue. Tape into place where needed.

6) Strip the PVA off the outside seam as soon as the resin hardens. The more you delay, the harder it gets. Remove sharp wrinkles and the built-up edge (if any) with a chisel or sandpaper.

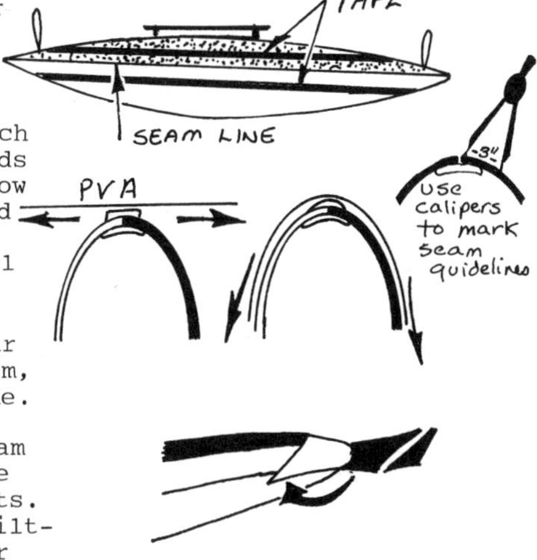

CAUTION: ANY ROUGHNESS remaining on the seam can cut your hands when you come in contact with the side of you boat during a roll or brace. Ruthlessly seek out and eliminate irregularities with sandpaper. If you don't, you'll do it later, after you have decorated the area with tiny bits of human skin.

END POURS:

A solid plug of resin adds considerable strength to the bow and stern, and seals the ends effectively at the same time. A few racers have omitted this, with unsatisfactory results, since this spot is quite difficult to seam effectively.The volume of the "pour" varies, depending on the design of the boat and its intended use. Here's what you need to do:

1) Estimate volume by holding a container (a dixie cup) next to the end of the boat. An end pour should go back 2"-3" on regular boats, more on narrow, pointier racing designs. Six ounces is a good "ballpark" estimate. Mix resin and add catalyst for a slow cure time (with the "esters") to avoid setting off the batch.

2) Add filler to resin to produce a thick, puttylike mix. For maximum durability, use fiberglass or Kevlar scraps; for light weight, use microbaloons. Plugs made from resin alone tend to crack and leak, so add something, even if its flour or talcum powder.

3) Set the boat on end, and look down into the bow or stern. Sometimes seam tape will be haphazzardly piled up. To fill the ends completely, you need to chip this back with a chisel attached to a broomhandle. A real #@&% !! of a job! Avoid this problem by measuring your seam tape so it ends a few inches from the tip.

4) Roll the resin/filler putty into a ball, and drop into the end of the boat. Poke and knead with a long stick so that air bubbles are removed, and the putty fills the end completely. Allow to cure.

5) Because of the length of a kayak or canoe, this process is usually done out-of-doors. To cure the plug in cold weather, add a bit more catalyst. The heat of the reaction will allow the cure to continue. If things slow down, you can put the end in a plastic bag and immerse it in a bucket of hot water. Watch the temperature closely; solid plugs can get mighty hot. You can control an overly "hot" reaction by immersing the plastic-bag covered end in cold water.

NOTE: Some people mix resin and filler to form a "slurry" rather than a putty. This is much harder to control; even a coordinated person will spill some of it on the sides of the boat. If you must use this technique, this dixie cup pouring system is recommended. The apparatus can be lowered into the boat, then inverted to put the mess right where you want it. Since resin-rich plugs generate more exothermic heat, cut back on the catalyst (50% of usual) and watch the reaction carefully.

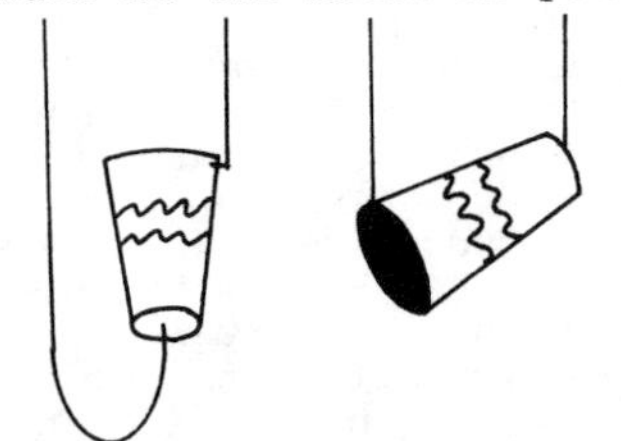

GRAB LOOPS are set into the bow and stern to make a boat rescueable, as its sleek shape allows for few other handholds. Since the loops are often anchored in the end pour, you should make your decision on how to do it before building your boat.

THE MOST COMMON TYPE TO DATE is a loop of 1/4" nlyon rope or ½" webbing set into the end pour via a hole drilled through it. Skimpy end pours, like those used by racers, are poorly suited to this technique. Be careful where you drill; if you miss the end pour, the hole will leak. The "fisherman's knot" used to join the ends is illustrated at right.

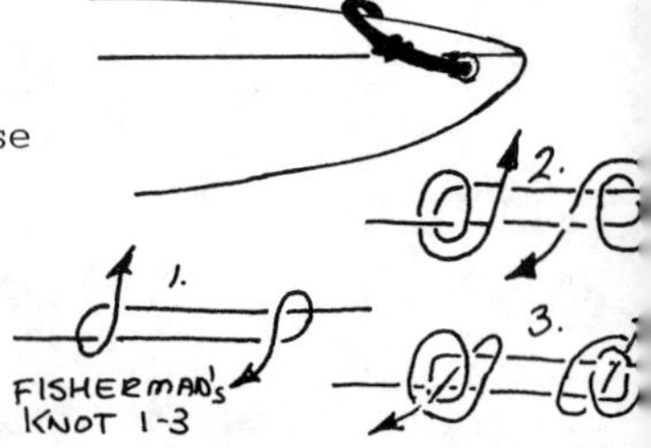

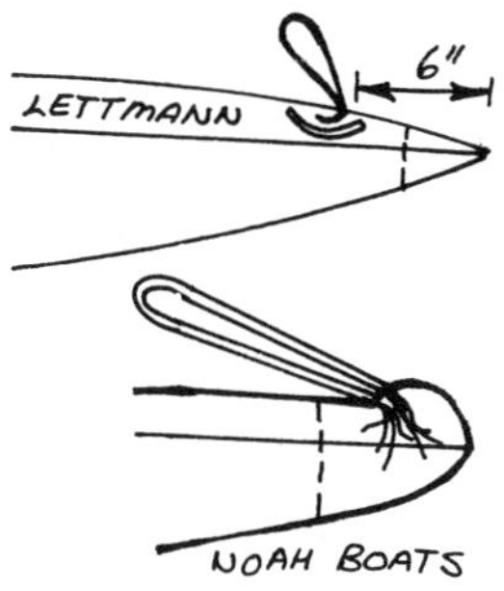

ANOTHER METHOD was developed by Klaus Lettmann and has since been widely imitated by others. It must be put in before the boat is seamed. Since it does not utilize the end pour, it is ideal for racers and pointy, low-volume boats. Simply drill a hole in the deck 6" back from the end, stick the rope through, fray the ends, and cover with glass cloth. (If the surrounding layup has cured, it should be sanded) Some molds have holes in the deck so that the loop can be placed during the layup.

A COMPROMISE TECHNIQUE, used by Noah Boats, involves drilling the hole where the end pours will be, sticking the frayed ends of the rope through, and pouring resin on top of them. Be sure to tape around the hole to prevent leaks. This does not work with pointed ends, but the designer of Noah Boats has blunted his ends slightly to allow extra room (illustrated), an outstanding innovation.

FOAM-TIPPED BOATS have been used occasionally on extreme designs to make them safer for other people who share the water. The technique for making one is simple: pour the ends as usual, then cut off the required amount (usually 2"). Take a piece of minicell or ethafoam, sculpt to shape, and glue into place. Follow up with tape if needed. This also absorbs considerable punishment, and might well be adapted to cruising boats for this reason.

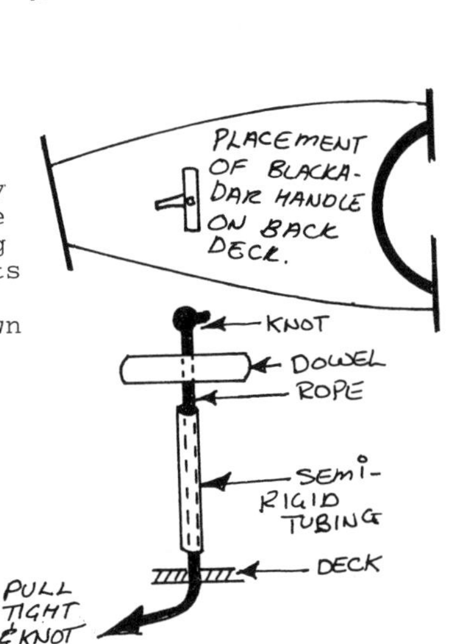

BLACKADAR HANDLE: This rescue handle was developed in Idaho for rescuing people in big water. The victim actually climbs partly onto the deck, and is able to breath in huge waves. Someone holding onto a grab loop, on the other hand, gets little air, and may be "clipped" under the chin as the stern bounces up and down in the waves. Collect a 6" length of broomhandle, 18" of ¼" nylon rope, and 4" of rigid polyethylene tubing with a ¼" inside diameter. Drill a hole in the center of the wood piece, and along the midline of the rear deck 2/3 of the way beck. Thread the rope through the handle, tubing, and then through the deck. Knot tightly or fiberglass in place. If you plan to do this, extra deck reinforcement is a good idea, particularly if your deck is lightweight.

PAINTERS, which are lengths of rope running from the stern (less commonly, the bow) grab loop to the cockpit, are out of fashion and not seen much. They can make boat rescue much easier, though, and frequent swimmers should consider them. I use the stern painter only (the bow line could catch a paddle and screw up your roll); about 5' of ¼" line is plenty. Tie a knot in the end, and tuck under your sprayskirt or (preferred) a shock cord loop, as illustrated. To make the loop, drill two holes 2-3" apart, push the shock cord through, and tie off each end. The painter is now out of the way, but instantly available.

COCKPIT RIMS:

A cockpit rim is a 4-5 layer all-glass layup which, when finished, allows you to attach a sprayskirt. It comes two ways: molded as part of a hanging seat, and laid up freehand. We will discuss both techniques, but a suggestion: be sure that you are dealing with a standard size. If you don't adjust now, you'll never be able to find a ready-made sprayskirt that fits! Here are a few hints:

1) USE BIAS-CUT STRIPS OF CLOTH when laying up complex forms like coamings and seats. These are pieces cut diagonally, across the weave. Bias-cut strips conform more readily to curves, making the job easier. Don't be afraid to use many overlapping scraps; there's no loss of strength and it allows you to make effective use of scraps. Strips 3-4" x 18" are ideal for cockpit rims; larger pieces may be needed for seats.

2) Rims and seats are laid up in the usual way. The sides of kayak seats and the front edge of the bottom take lots of punishment, and require extra reinforcement. Carbon fiber is recommended for light layups.

3) Rims and seats are difficult to "pop" when fully cured, but if attacked early they are quite flexible and the job goes quicker. Popsicle sticks make great wedges.

4) Trimming is easiest when done early. I use an excellent pair of offset sheet metal shears in preference to a knife, and do the job after removing the seat from the mold. Use a Surform file, followed by sandpaper, to finish the job.

NOTE: COCKPIT RIMS, LIKE ALL ACCESSORIES, must be installed only on a prepared surface. If the layup has cured, vigorous hand sanding of the underside (until the fibers show) is mandatory. Otherwise, you will have leaks. Points of attachment on hanging seats should also be sanded in the same way.

INSTALLING HANGING SEATS:

Hanging seats, such as the K-1 and C-1 versions shown at right, nest into a portion of the deck called the chimney which curves up to meet it. The tighter the fit, the easier the installation job. Here's how to do it.

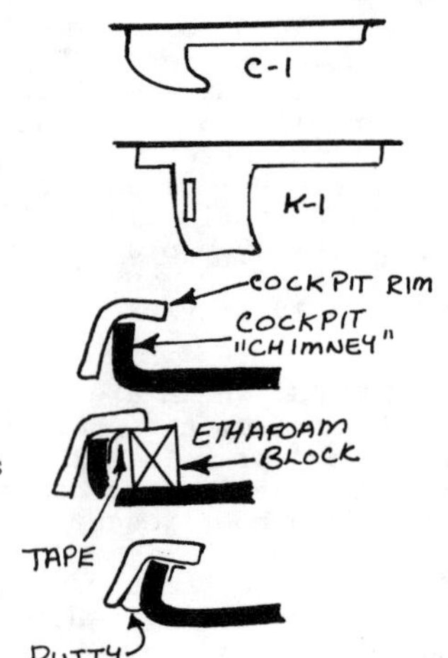

1) Set the hanging seat (or plain rim) into the chimney. Adjust the height, and support with ethafoam scraps. The rim must be high and wide enough to catch the spraycover, and this means about 3/4" high x 3/4" overhang. Tape the gap between the two.
2) Make up a putty using a) microballoons b) cab-o-sil c) milled fibers (or use body putty). Add catalyst, and force into the gap between the rim and the chimney with a putty knife until full. Check your work, particularly behind the seat.
3) For a heat cure, wrap pipe heater tape underneath the rim.

This installation is most easily done when seaming out of the mold before joining the deck and hull. If this is impossible, suspend the mold cockpit down at shoulder height. Put putty and tools in easy reach, and don't forget to cover your hair.

DEALING WITH SLOPPY FITTING RIMS: If the fit of your coaming in the chimney is poor, you'll have to use a lot of putty and the rim will be susceptable to damage. Here's how to cope with the problem:

1) Fill the entire space between the chimney and the seat with putty or milled fibers. Allow a full cure.

2) Grind rim, filler and boat to form a continuous smooth surface for the application of fiberglass cloth. Mix resin and apply 3 layers of bias-cut fiberglass. The area behind the seat can be covered with fiberglass running from the sides to the deck.

WHEN A RIM MOLD IS NOT AVAILABLE, as is the case with most C-Boats, get a seven-foot length of 3/4" Dia. plastic tubing or (better) a strip of minicell shaped with sandpaper to the ideal shape. Either one can be attached with contact cement or hot glue; place material around the rim and cut to length. The cockpit should be roughed up thoroughly with sandpaper. Cut a good number of strips of bias-cut fiberglass, lay on wax paper, and saturate with resin. Set the boat on its side, and drape the cloth over the tubing and under the deck. Build up 4-6 layers of fiberglass, allow them to gel solidly, then flip the boat over and do the other side. (If the first half of the rim is no longer sticky, you'll need to sand the area where the two "halves" will overlap. When the second half gels hard enough to cut, remove the tubing and trim with sheet metal shears. Allow a minimum of 3/4" overhang so that the skirt will stay on. Don't wait for a full cure, as this will make the job much tougher.

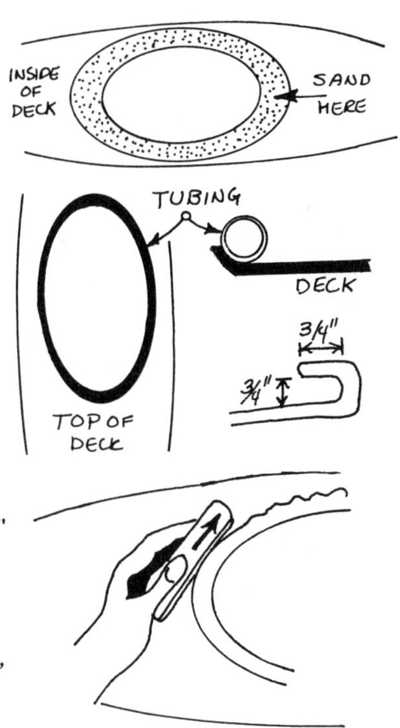

FINISHING: Once the rim has been attached, the edge and underside must be carefully finished so that it will not tear either you or your spraycover. Using a Surform file, cut the rim back so that it does not overlap by more than 3/4", then round off the sharp edges with medium grit sandpaper until it feels smooth. Check the underside for sharp, cutting fiberglass shards and rough resined areas, particularly at the thigh brace area of the cockpit rim in kayaks. Smooth any offending areas. Remove any Ethafoam scraps or putty which may remain under the rim. Check for leaks, and patch with body putty or fiberglass cloth. Minor leaks can be patched with resin or butyl caulk.

FLOTATION:

Fiberglass does not float on its own, so some kind of flotation is essential. In kayaks and C-1's this has usually taken the shape of specially-fitted air bags. This maximizes buoyancy and decreases damage in the event of an upset. Air bags alone are fine for touring kayaks; however, indestructable boats and daring paddlers have lead to increased entrapment danger during a pin. For this reason, full-length foam walls have become standard equipment for kayaks in this country. While their main purpose is to maintain the shape of the boat during a pin, walls have other advantages. These include adding rigidity to the deck and hull and reducing strain on the seam during pop-ups and enders. But getting caught in the boat is a major concern; smart paddlers know that their life may depend on their walls and take pains to install them properly.

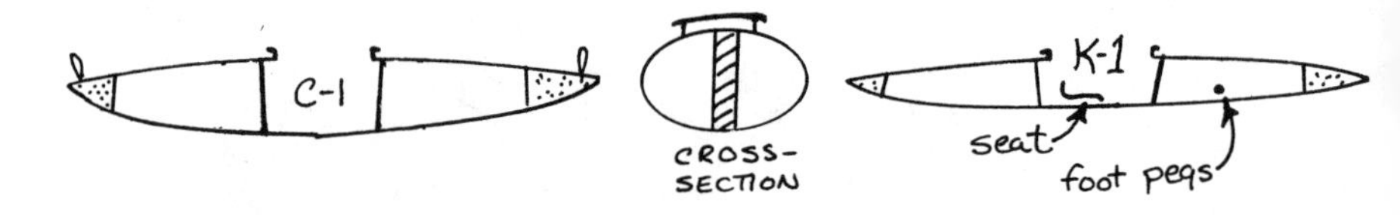

THE ABOVE DIAGRAMS show how walls are installed in canoes and kayaks. Larger kayakers should be careful that full-length front walls do not interfere with a fast exit; a heavier deck and a "partial" front wall ending 6" past the footpegs may make more sense. "Partial" front and rear walls which extended about a foot behind the cockpit (and in front of the cockpit in C-1's) allowed the use of"full"(as opposed to"split")air bags. As split bags have become more available, this variant has lost popularity except among those who confine themselves to rapids of less than Class III difficulty. C-boaters often use their walls as seats or as an anchor for other outfitting. Read further in the "outfitting" section for details.

CUTTING ETHAFOAM is not difficult. A bread knife, hacksaw blade, or sabre saw with a long blade all work well. The problem lies in figuring out the proper shape. If you're lucky, you may be able to find someone with templates for walls. Old walls from the same design boat also make good templates. If not, one method is to take inside measurements at 6" intervals, then cutting a tad oversized to allow a margin for error and to allow for the compression needed in a tight fit. If you need more height, additional foam can be glued on the ends of the wall with little loss of strength.

THE PLUMB-BOB Method of obtaining a template was developed by Wally Williams of the AMC/Boston Chapter and is perhaps the fastest and most reliable way to do the job. The boat is suspended over a sheet of brown paper and the string of a plumb-bob run along its sides. As the string is moved, an assistant marks the path of the plumb-bob with a series of dots. These dots, once connected, form the outline of the template. As with any untested pattern, it's best to cut a bit oversized at first until you are sure of it. Save the pattern or (better yet) give it to the mold owner for future use.

REMOVABLE WALLS can be fashioned to permit access to the back of a kayak, allowing the use of full storage flotation for kayaking. 3-4 layers of fiberglass cloth are laid against waxed foam to form a "track". When trimmed, these pieces will guide the walls and hold them in place.

FOAM BULKHEADS set across the hull have been used by some paddlers in place of bags. They also provide some deck support. Because water can collect behind these structure, we recommend that they be used in combination with removable plugs in the bow and stern. The disadvantage is that the inside of the boat is not available for gear storage. Cutting foam to an exact cross section is a real pain. Use cardboard templates, then cut the piece slightly oversized so you can recover from your mistakes. It can then be installed the same way as regular walls. Remove the drain plugs when crossing mountain passes, or you may blow out your bulkhead. (it pays to let some air out of float bags, too, for the same reason.)

INSTALLATION INSTRUCTIONS:

1) Your best choices for glue are resin or a panelling adhesive called Liquid Nails (my first choice). Contact cement grabs with the slightest touch and is unsuitable for work in such tight places. Do not use Polyester or Vinylester with styrofoam; the styrene in it will dissolve the foam.

   NOTE: It goes without saying that you should try your wall for fit beforehand. The time to correct problems is NOT after smearing glue all over the edges!

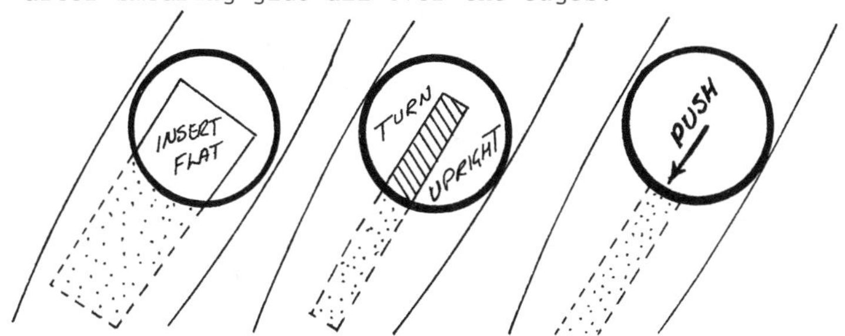

2) Coat the edges of the walls or bulkheads liberally with resin. Insert the wall horizontally through the cockpit hole, the narrow end first. With the wall half in the cockpit opening and half in the boat, turn it so that it is vertical. With the wall being tapered, and thus undersized in its current position, there should be little or no resistance to this.

3) Push the wall into the boat until it is in place. The resin acts as a lubricant, minimizing friction. If the wall is "off" to one side, it can be moved with a 5-6 foot length of pipe. Insert the pipe into the boat, putting one end into the bow or stern. By pulling towards the center with this pipe, you have the ideal lever for repositioning walls.

4) Firmly support the boat, and pile bricks on the deck to press the fiberglass against the foam. Allow to cure.

OUTFITTING:

"Outfitting" means attaching whatever system of blocks, seats, pads, and straps are needed to permit the paddler to hold himself inside the boat when bounced and hassled by tricky currents. Please note that I said "hold himself"! As boats get smaller, many paddlers become tempted to wedge themselves into designs which are much too tight for comfort and safety. This is a very dangerous, if not potentially fatal practice, since you must be able to part company with your boat quickly in many situations. We have had several narrow excapes in high-level racing among paddlers who ought to know better. Another potential hazard involves fittings which allow the boater to slide forward after a collision.You may look funny sitting "up to your armpits" in a kayak, but you're also completely helpless. We stress safety in this chapter, and recommendations are based on other people's mistakes. Ignor them at your peril !

PLEASE NOTE: Whenever fittings are to be attached to the boat using resin and cloth, the point of attachment on both the fitting and the boat must be thoroughly sanded until the cloth fibers which make up the respective part show through. You can glue (or even tape) fittings to a boat without these preliminaries, but the bond does not hold up as well. To save space, this admonition will not be repeated over and over in the forthcoming section !

KAYAK OUTFITTING:

A kayakist holds himself inside his boat by pressing his knees against the deck into thigh braces, maintaining this pressure by pushing off foot braces with his toes. Back and lateral support needed for leaning is provided by the seat, which is built up to fit the paddler's hips snugly.

HANGING SEATS are suspended from the cockpit rim. They must be supported and modified to fit the individual paddler, and to minimize wear and tear on the boat, as follows:

BLOCKING THE SEAT is needed to keep the seat from shifting from side to side as you lean the boat and to provide a pad between the bottom of the boat and the seat. Otherwise, the weight of the boater will stress the rim/deck joint, causing leaks, and when the bottom of the boat crashes against the seat (as when "ski-jumping" rocks) it will do more damage on the inside than on the outside. The best way to "block" a seat is with scraps of Ethafoam cut and placed as shown. Some enlightened manufacturers are using pieces of fiberglass (curved slightly so they'll absorb shock like a spring) to do the same thing, but this is beyond the reach of most homebuilders.

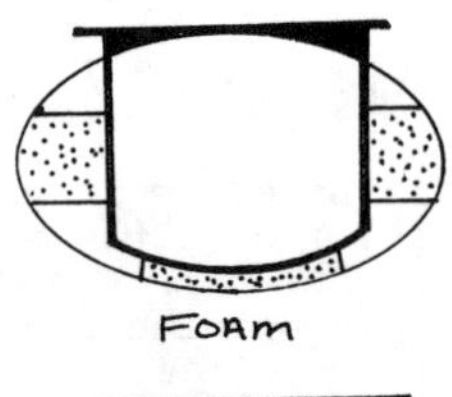

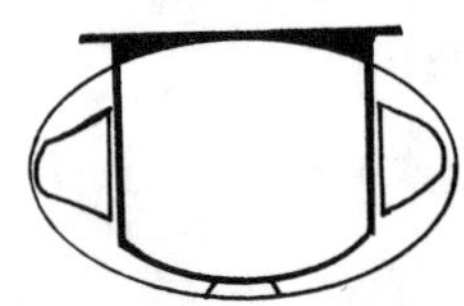

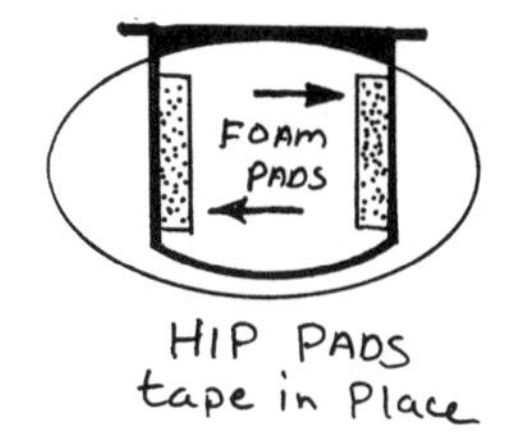

FITTING THE SEAT: Kayak seats come in only one size, but for maximum performance their sides must fit snugly against your hips. When this is not true, bracing and rolling are difficult. To get a perfect fit, take Ethafoam or some other foam, cut hip pads of the proper size and thickness, then tape or glue in place. BE SURE to allow a bit of extra room if you wear a wetsuit, and NEVER wedge yourself in like a cork.

Kayak seats are rigid, but people aren't. Some people find that a seat's contours cause discomfort or even numbness. If the front edge of the seat cuts into you, trim it back. Other areas can be padded with foam as needed. Keep experimenting until you're comfortable !

A BACK STRAP increases both comfort and security, for a paddler can now put the pressure needed on toe blocks and thigh straps without pushing himself off the seat. Also keeps your back from being slammed against the rear of the cockpit rim in heavy turbulence. Use nylon seat belt webbing (purchased for very little money from an auto graveyard) cut to length and slipped through vertical slits cut in the sides of the seat. Tie or sew in place; if you use a buckle, be sure to pad it.

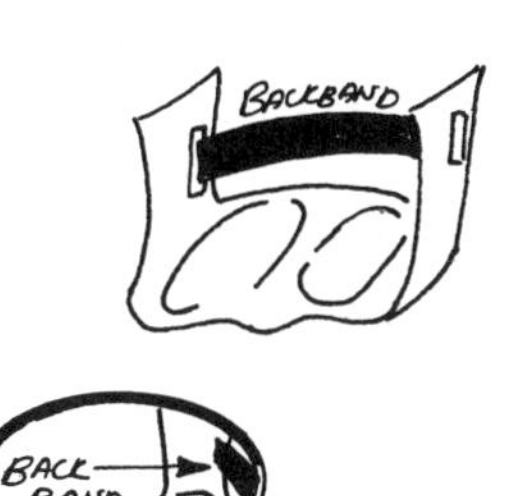

ADJUSTABLE SEATS permit the paddler to move his weight forward or back to control fore and aft trim. They are especially important for squirt boat paddlers, or those carrying a lot of weight when touring. You can makethem from a standard seat mold, first laying up the rim and a part of the sides, then laying up the seat high enough so it will overlap. Adjustment is via round-head butterfly screws. Blocking the seat is difficult, so lay it up extra-heavy for maximum rigidity.

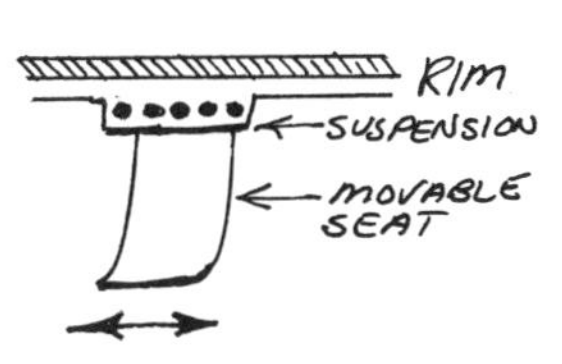

IF A SEPARATE SEAT is used, it should rest on a sculptured piece of Ethafoam and be glued in place. If hip support is not sufficient, the sides can be built up with Ethafoam. One possible method is shown at right.

TO ATTACH A HANGING SEAT TO AN EXISTING RIM, lay up the seat and sides, then affix to the rim with pop-rivets as shown. Note how a bit of rim is also laid up so that the assembly "hooks" in place. Block this seat as usual.

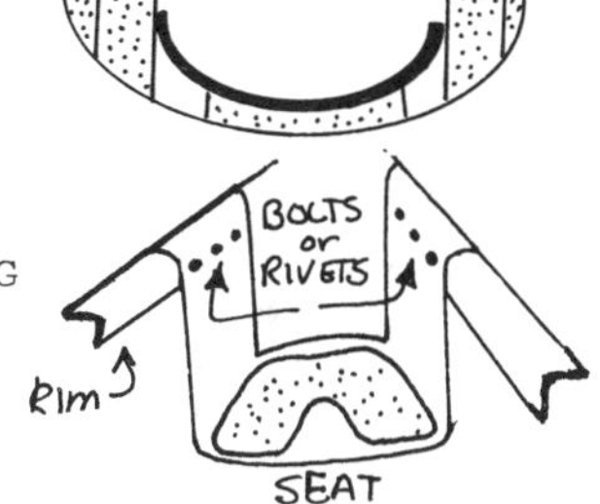

IF NO SEAT MOLD IS AVAILABLE, or if you are too broad across the behind to fit the ones that are, a workable substitute can be made from 2" Ethafoam. Make a box as shown. Contour the bottom of the box to fit your rump. On the bottom, cut a "+" groove pattern to fit a similar pattern of ribs and keels built into your boat. This will keep the sheet from shifting. For security, block the sides, except for casual flatwater paddlers, who can safely eliminate the sides altogether.

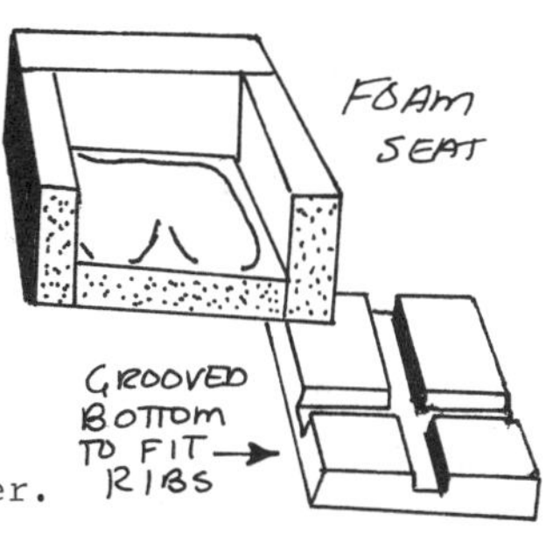

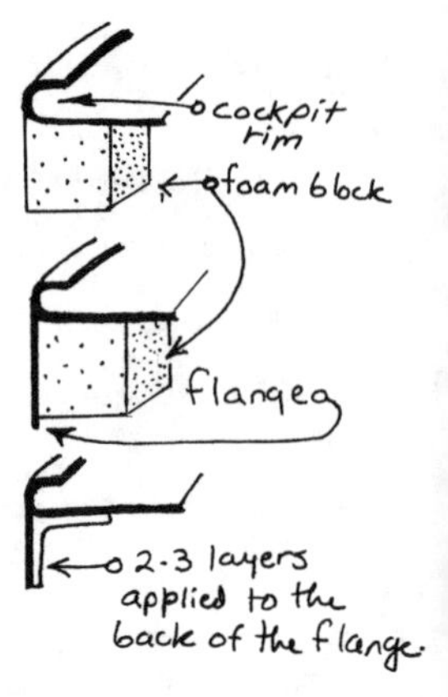

TO FIT A HANGING SEAT to a kayak which has an existing rim, you'll have to fabricate an attaching flange. Glue a piece of foam faced with wax paper or PVA sheet to the underside of the deck so that the edge lines up with the inside of the cockpit rim where you want the seat to hang. Lay up 4-5 layers of fiberglass against the foam and over the coaming. When the resin has cured, remove the foam and sand everything smooth. Now apply 2-3 layers of fiberglass on the back of the flange between it and the seat. Allow to cure, then trim to shape. You can now install the seat like the adjustable type described previously.

CAUTION: In low volume boats, stability is greatly effected by seat height. Get the seat as low as possible for best handling qualities.

KNEE PADS are usually combined with THIGH BRACES, which in most modern designs consist of indentations or convolutions built into the deck. On older designs, which lack these "knee bumps", separate "thigh braces" are usually molded and glassed in place. These pieces are quite a nuisance, though, and today most people do without them. Blocks of ethafoam glued in place make an excellent substitute. Pad all these places with neoprene, ethafoam, or something else which is soft.

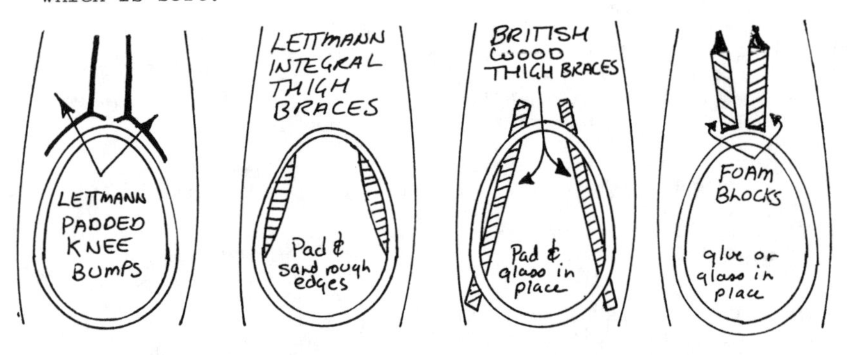

Many hanging seat/cockpit rim combinations have thigh braces built into the design. These are great for smaller people, but if they interfere with a bigger paddler's wet exit, they should be removed or trimmed back. Sometimes there are no thigh braces, but because the boat is being used by a smallish person, additional support is desired. English "wood strip" thigh braces utilize 2"x3/4" lengths of wood fiberglassed in place as shown above. Always be sure that the arrangement you use allows for a fast underwater exit in case of trouble.

NOTE: When installing padding, use contact cement; resin hardens the foam.

FOOTBRACES: In the early years of kayaking, these were something of a problem. Most people used glassed-in structures made of foam or metal. They never held; failures were frequent and setting them in the correct position was a constant headache. We now use bolt-in systems almost exclusively. The most popular design is by Yakima Products of Arcata, California; there are, however, a number of acceptable competitors.

YAKIMA FOOT BRACES, available through many white water outfitters, are the the number-one choice of the nation's best manufacturers and custom builders. Made from aluminum extrusions, it is fully adjustable, surprisingly lightweight, quite strong, and simple to install. The track has a self-cleaning notch to permit sand particles to fall out before they jam the track. There are two lengths: 10" and 13". Since adjustability is important, I'd always opt for the longer length. Like all aluminum products, it's susceptable to corrosion in salt water. Rinse them off with fresh water after each use.

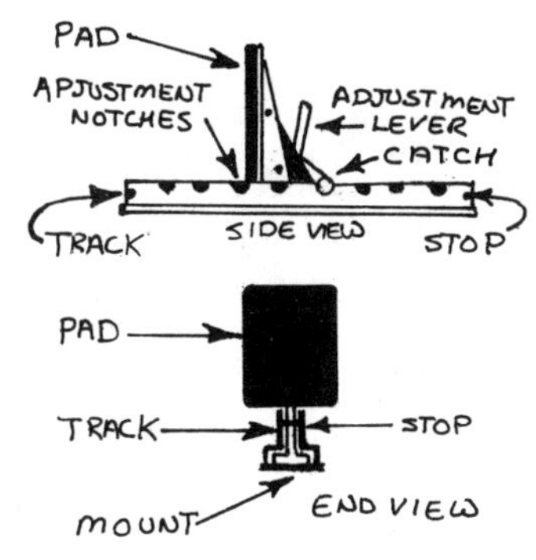

Installation of this and other brands is simple. First, sit inside your kayak, and have someone mar the position of your feet. The holes are drilled below the seam line; measure the distance apart for spacing. You can judge for yourself where in the range of adjustment you want to be so that you'll be able to share or sell your boat.

NON-ADJUSTABLE FOOT BRACES are sometimes made from fiberglass or metal. The multi-step type allows some adjustability. These are bolted in place. Because of adhesion problems, nobody really fiberglasses them in place anymore.

BAR-TYPE FOOTBRACES are preferred by many racers because they allow you to shift your feet around as you paddle. They have, however, been linked to a number of entrapment deaths in Europe, and only the fail-safe footrest bar should be used. This device, developed by Valley Canoe Products, England, uses a bar which is held firmly in place with foot-pressure, yet will hinge back should a foot become wedged behind it, allowing the paddler to work free.

The flanges can be laid up in the hull on a cardboard and waxed paper mold (shown; 5-8 layers of glass required), or aluminum angle iron can be bent into shape and bolted into place (harder). The bar can be made from aluminum or wood (broken paddle shafts are great) slotted to go over the flange. The flange is then drilled to accept bolts; one serves as the pivot, the other as the stop. Note how the holes are drilled in the flange so that the bar will not contact the sides of the boat, even when moved forward into the tapered end. Check for smooth operation before using.

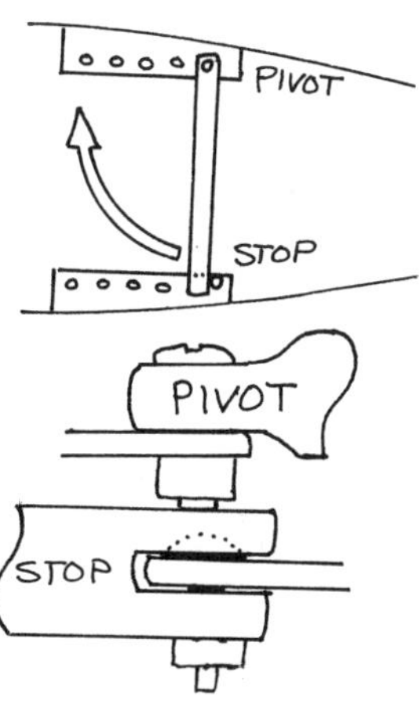

Adapted from Byde: Canoe Building

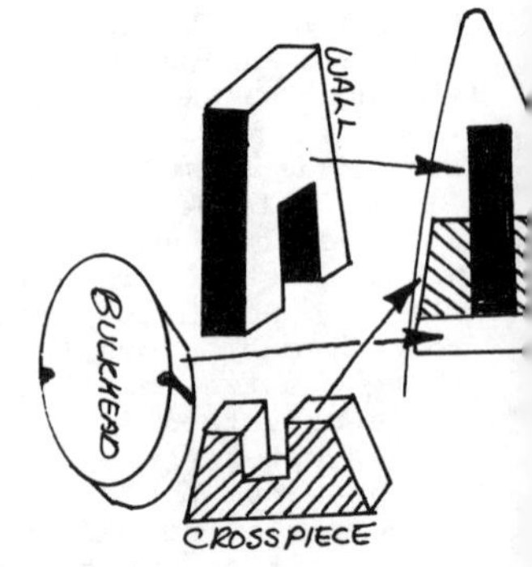

ETHAFOAM BULKHEADS make excellent foot-braces. Once installed, they wedge themselves tighter after each impact. With low volume boats, including squirt boats with decks so low that the user has to point his toes, filling the bow with foam provides reliable support and flotation in one package. Other bulkheads can be hung from brackets bolted to the sides of the kayak, or a vertical wall can be mated to a crosspiece. If properly cut and fitted, no glue is needed.

The advantage of bulkheads is they absorb shock,protecting the paddler's knees and ankles. The disadvantage is that they will compress over time, so be prepared to glue on more foam as needed.

A TRAPEZE BAR makes an excellent backup for expeditions. It is suspended from the hanging seat and a loop along the seam line near the feet. The latter feature keeps the amount of loose line under control, minimizing the danger of entanglement. Drilll the proper holes and set the loops beforehand, and carry the bar elsewhere until needed.

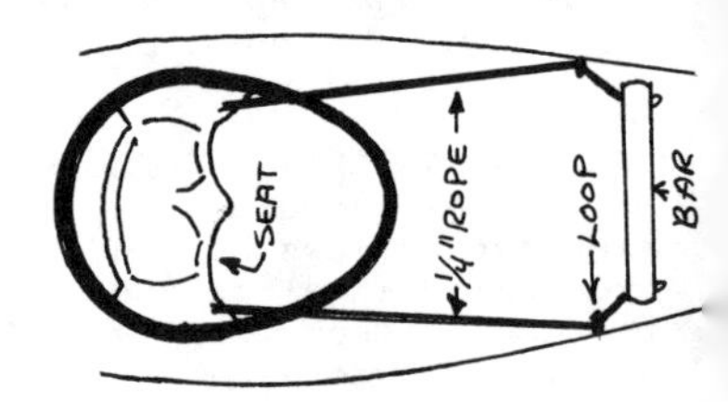

OUTFITTING DECKED CANOES:

Canoeists hold themselves inside their boat with pressure against their thigh braces created by squeezing their knees together. The position of their knees is maintained by 1) contoured knee pads; 2) a firm seat 3) toe blocks. The latter are placed so that the paddler must release them with his foot to back out of the thigh straps and work free of the boat. Ideally, weight should be distributed evenly between your seat and your knees. The positioning of these fittings is quite individual; test them before final installation.

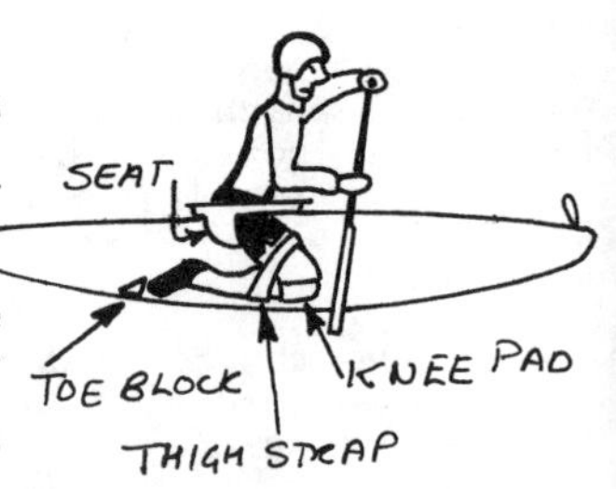

THERE ARE MANY KINDS of C-1 seats available, but the most important consideration is <u>height</u>. Racers prefer a 5"-7" seat because it lowers their center of gravity and improves control while cruisers, who are in their boat for longer periods, prefer the comfort of a 7"-9" seat. The bigger the boater, the higher the seat needs to be. There is one catch: a too-high seat makes for an unstable boat which is almost impossible to roll. Anything over 9" is too high no matter what the design; for low-volume racing boats, 7" is the absolute maximum. If your seat is jacked up to the maximum and you're still uncomfortable, it might be a good idea to consider an open boat or a kayak.

HANGING SEATS come in many configurations. Like kayak seats, they hang from the rim. Properly padded, they provide outstanding control and lateral support. But unfortunately, most were designed for the average European paddler, who weighs around 165 lb. Bigger people find them too low and too tight for comfort; furthermore, they have an unnerving tendancy to catch feet at the wrong time. The seat itself is under too much pressure to be unsupported, so extend the ethafoam wall underneath it so it has something to hang on besides the rim.

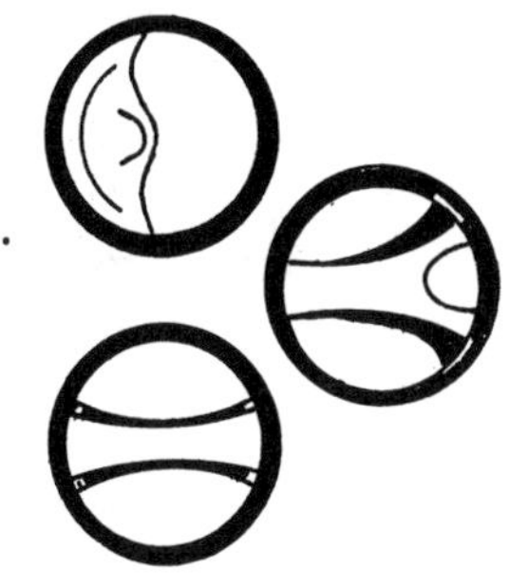

THWARTS were carried over from open boats. They allow really close control, but are uncomfortable and can catch feet during fast bail-outs. Start with a clear pine 1"x3"; varnish it, shim it to the proper height (angled slightly forward, and canted to your preferred paddling side for comfort), then bolt in place (pad bolt tops to avoid cuts). Very low thwarts must be fiberglassed in place, as shims wider than 3" are easily broken. Wedge between seams, & cover ends with fiberglass.

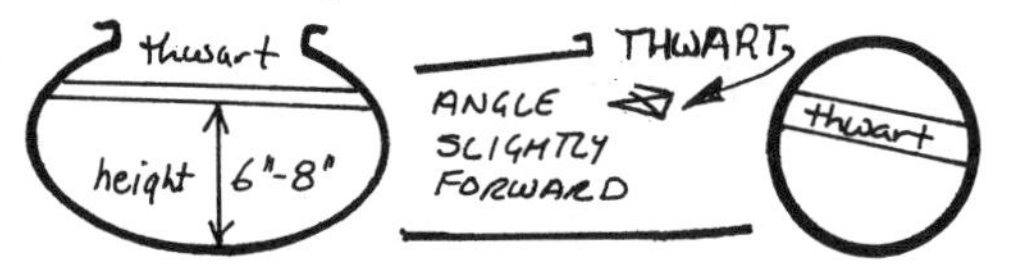

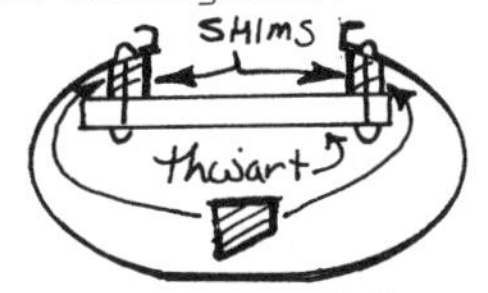

PEDESTAL SEATS are carved from Ethafoam and are preferred by cruising paddlers because 1) they are comfortable and 2) they do not get in the way of a fast exit. They are particularly good for big-footed types who have trouble with other systems. There are two basic configurations and innumerable variations; both use 2" ethafoam sheets glued together with resin or contact cements. People with sensitive behinds may want to widen the seats an inch or two, so long as it does not interfere with their excape. DO NOT eliminate the back portion (or the front portion in the straight-through design), since it serves to anchor the unit and keep it from wobbling from side to side.

THIGH BRACES AND KNEE CUPS help the paddler maintain a solid, well-balanced position in the boat. The knee cups should be placed as far apart as possible while still being comfortable. (Big paddlers may have to increase the cockpit size in low volume boats to allow a shoulder-wide stance) The cups help prevent shifting when bounced around, but the thigh straps actually hold the paddler inside the boat. These cut diagonally across the thighs, so that the paddler can maintain his position by squeezing slightly against them. As anyone who has paddled an open canoe can tell you, this really increases control while cutting fatigue at the same time.

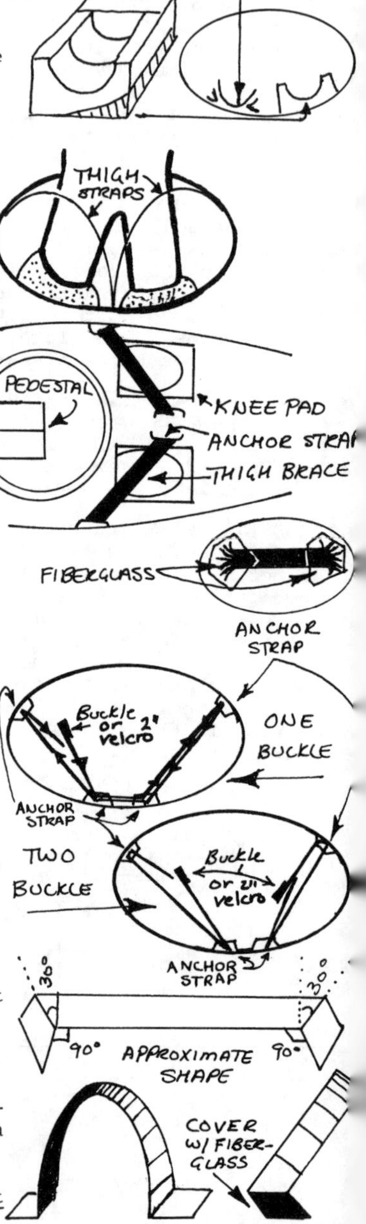

KNEE CUPS are better than plain pads because they give support as well as protection. Cut from Ethafoam as shown; sit in the boat and mark the positions; then glue in place with contact cement or resin. A few paddlers have used a molded fiberglass form padded and fiberglassed in place. These are particularly good in wildwater boats, where the cups are actually perched on the sides rather than resting on the bottom. Once these are installed, you're ready to attach the thigh braces.

THIGH STRAPS are made from 2" nylon webbing threaded through loops of nylon webbing or rope imbedded in the hull called anchor straps. Four anchor straps are needed: two about 2"-3" to the side of the keel line a few inches behind the knee and two more at the seam line about level with the boater's crotch. Sand these places thoroughly, then take 4"-6" lengths of rope or (preferred) webbing, fray the ends for about 1" back, lay in place parallel to the keel or seam, and cover with 4-6 layers of resin-saturated fiberglass cloth. Put wax paper under the loop, then saturate the rope also. This makes the strap stiffer, causing them to exert less peel force at the point of attachment which in turn makes it harder to pull it loose. (It also prevents the fiberglass anchors from cutting through the rope or webbing)

The straps themselves can be set in two ways, as illustrated at right. The two-buckle approach is more convenient than the one-buckle approach. Velcro can be substituted for buckles; allow at least a 6" overlap and 1½" of velcro built up by laying strips of 1/2" or 3/4" velcro next to each other. If you are using a buckle or D-rings, pad them, or set them so that they will not rest on your thigh when the straps are tightened.

MACHINES are rigid aluminum strips bent to form rigid thigh braces. They are preferred by racers because they give excellent control, but they are often the victims of metal fatigue and break at inconvenient times. (For expeditionary use, set anchor straps, and carry a thigh strap as a back-up) Putting them in requires considerable patience and experimentation; they must be bent just right for comfort.

Buy two strips of .090 aluminum 1½"x24" (J.R. Sweet sells this) Bend as shown in the illustration; the 90° bends should be done over a radius rather than an angle for maximum durability.

When bent into a bow, the "thigh loops" should angle slightly forward; fit them to your thighs by bending them as you kneel in the boat. Adjust length and fit as needed. Take your time; once these babies are installed they can't be moved. Pad with neoprene, and attach with fiberglass cloth. The bottom bend is critical: John Sweet, who uses machines exclusively, says that all failures he's seen have been due to a too-sharp bend at the point of attachment to the hull.

Machines can be made from nylon webbing attached to the hull directly (using the same metheod as anchor straps), laid up over a mold (a wax-paper covered thigh), saturated with resin, and left to cure. A three-layer nylon/glass layup has also been used, but this is a lot more work. Neither metheod is especially popular.

BULKHEAD MACHINES combine knee pads and machines in a single, easily installed package. The bulkhead is cut to fit the cross section of the boat just ahead of the cockpit. If you don't make a cardboard template first (and maybe even if you do), you're going to waste a lot of foam ! Once the bulkhead fits, cut some knee holes, and slowly expand them until they fit you perfectly across the thighs. Glue an extra piece of Ethafoam under the knees for support, and an extra piece at the top for additional thigh purchase if needed. Cut drain holes at the deck peak and keel line so that water does not collect behind the bulkhead. Coat the edges with resin, and push into place. A full (or even a partial) ethafoam wall will keep the bulkhead from being pushed forward, and permit standard air bags to be used. NOTE: this type of outfitting is not good for expeditions, since it renders the front of the boat totally inaccessible.

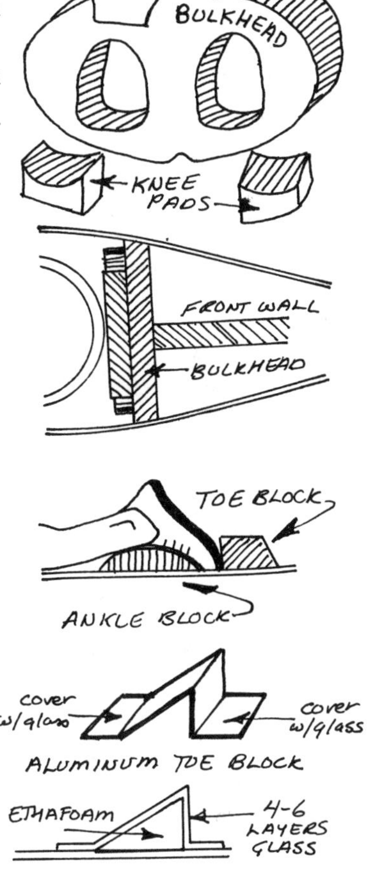

TOE BLOCKS give the boater something to push forward on, so that he can slide into the thigh straps and stay there, yet release himself in an instant. They should be placed so that when the boater is in the right position, his extended toes barely touch the blocks. This way, they can get you back in position without causing constant discomfort when you paddle. Sometimes this arrangement puts a funny "kink" in the paddler's ankle joint, decreasing circulation and causing pain. An ethafoam <u>ankle block</u>, which supports the instep and keeps your foot in a more natural position, can easily be installed. Don't suffer; experiment until you are comfortable.

Toe blocks can be made from 1) a triangular piece of ethafoam covered with 5-6 layers of fiberglass 2) an aluminum strip bent to the proper shape and fiberglassed in place. Check the placement carefully <u>before</u> permanently attaching the blocks, wearing the shoes you plan to wear. Ankle blocks are cut by trial and error, then glued in "as is." If they keep coming out, use a layer or two of fiberglass, and pad with neoprene.

PEDESTAL SEAT-TOE BLOCK COMBOS are solid and effective. Cut the pedestal as before, leaving room at the bottom for an additional layer of foam. Cut the bottom piece as shown, and attach it to the canoe. You can now slide the pedestal into place. The best way to get a perfect fit on the toe blocks is to cut them long, then trim them back after installation. They are one piece with the pedestal, and will never come loose.

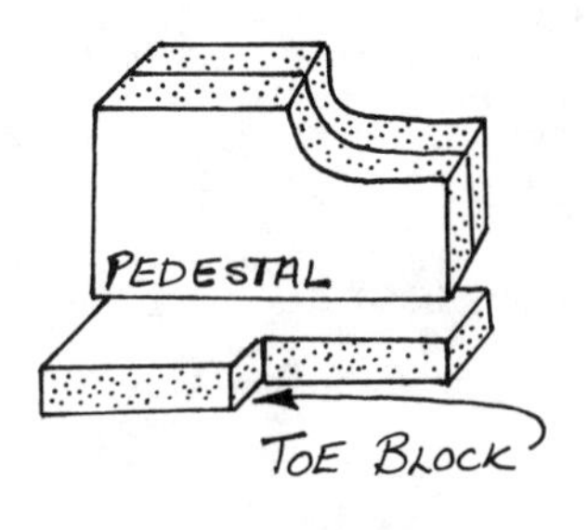

YAKIMA FOOTBRACES make excellent adjustable toe blocks, and are especially popular with open boat paddlers. Remove the bolts, and drill out the screw holes on one of the two footbraces. A long screw will run through these enlarged holes, through the pedestal, and finally screws into the footpegs on the opposite side. When tightened, it's a very secure installation.

STRAIGHT-THROUGH PEDESTALS can serve as anchors for both thigh straps and toe blocks. The thigh strap anchor is a hole lined with aluminum pipe; you thread your strap through the hole. The toe block can be Yakima footbraces (see above) or a length of 1" dowel pushed through the pedestal at the proper location. Both are strong and difficult to dislodge.

SPARE PADDLES can be carried by C-boat paddlers on their front or back deck. A loop of shock cord or (better) ½" rubber rope is stretched between two holes in the deck to hold the blade in place. Unless you have access to a dwarf, do this before you put in the other fittings, or even before you seam the two halves together. Securing the T-grip is much more difficult; I recommend the handy "clip" illustrated at right. To lay one up, first line up some objects (a pencil, a paperbacked book) and tape them to a board as shown. Cover with wax paper, then lay 4-8 layers of fiberglass on top of it. When the resin has cured, peel off the paper and trim into 1½"-2" wide strips. The thicker the laminate, the more rigid and stronger the clip will be. Bolt in place. The diagram shows how the clip releases the paddle.

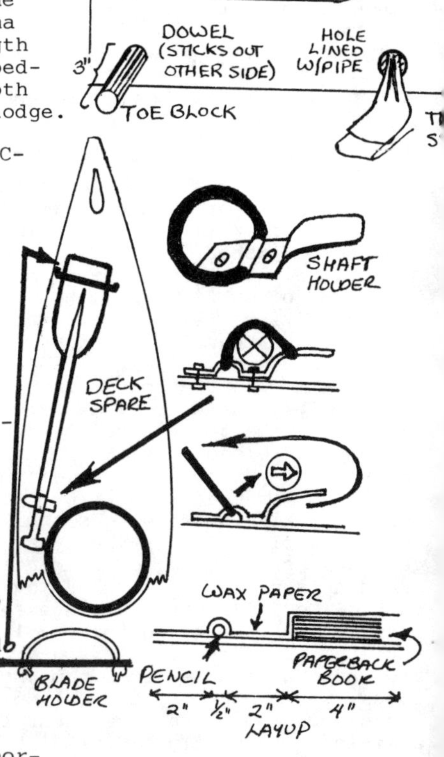

SMALL GEAR AND CAMERA BAGS are normally carried just behind the seat in kayaks. The seat itself offers ample opportunities for tying-in. Canoeists are not so lucky. The best place for a small bag is between your legs, tied down to an anchor strap. If this strap is not available, make one, using the technique described in the section on thigh straps.

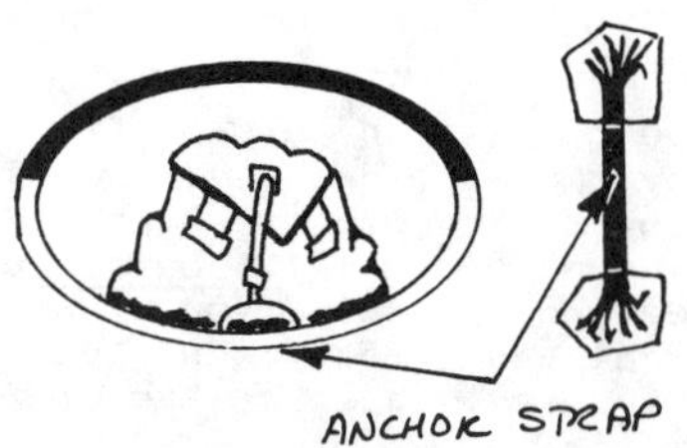

BUILDING OPEN CANOES:

Open canoes are coming back. Once thought of as a stepping stone to a kayak or decked canoe, experienced paddlers are re-discovering their simplicity and challenge. Streams formerly off limits are now regularly run. New, sleeker designs allow faster travel in flat water and unheard-of agility in rapids. Competition in slalom, downriver, and marathon (not to mention poling) is becoming increasingly intense. New designs are constantly being introduced, while the "old standbys" remain for family tripping and other less demanding uses. As a result, more and more people are building their own.

There are three classes of open canoes:

STANDARD HULLS based on commercially available models.

HIGH-PERFORMANCE HULLS based on the USCA cruiser and other more efficient shapes, this is the choice of the experienced paddler for long-distance cruising and racing. The more extreme designs ("Pro Boats") require more skill than some of the family canoe/ marathon boat compromises.

SLALOM HULLS are a relatively new innovation. These are usually high-side versions of slalom C-1's and C-2's used for slalom racing. They can, however, open up a new range of possibilities to the cruiser. But beware: their short length makes them more prone to swamp.

HULL LAYUP can be tricky; open canoes are large boats with wide, flat areas which are not easily made rigid. Many commercial canoes are quite heavy because the manufacturer uses many layers (5-8) to end up with a boat which does not oilcan; ie: flex in at the center. Unless you want a 70-80 pound boat, you're going to have to be more crafty. A full keel-strip and evenly placed ribs will make a four-layer boat sufficiently rigid for racing; for extended cruises, the extra layer will be well worth the trouble. Kevlar will lower the weight of any boat substantially. An extra layer in the bottom is essential for rigidity and for boats with deep bows and little rocker, extensive reinforcement in the bow (4-6 layers) is essential. The edges should also be reinforced to give the frame additional purchase (see relevant sections of this book for details).

Many of the top manufacturers are putting a layer of Airex foam or hexel honeycomb material into the bottom to add rigidity without excessive weight. The stuff is melted into shape with a heat-gun and covered with resin. But beware: most are very hard to install properly without vacuum-bagging, and almost every foam will absorb huge quantities of resin unless properly treated. The usual thickness used is 1/16 of an inch. Consult your supplier for advice on what to do with your particular resin system.

The new slalom hulls are made in a regular C-1 or C-2 mold with an extension attached to the flange. The same layups that are used for decked boats can be used with confidence on these smaller craft. A mold which is not equipped with an extension can have a temporary one built from cardboard, covered with wax paper, and taped in place.

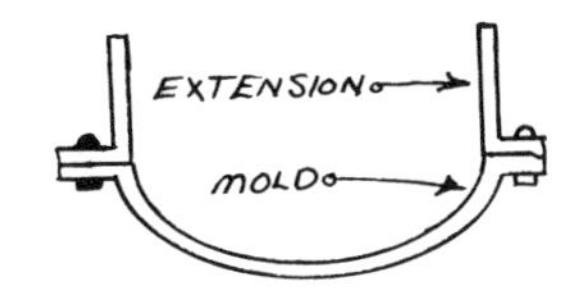

THE SUPERSTRUCTURE is best thought of as a series of triangles: the one formed by the thwart, ribs and keel, and the one formed by the gunwales and the thwarts. If any of these parts are broken or left out, the canoe is substantially weaker.

THWARTS should be placed with an eye for 1) solo paddling 2) tandem paddling, and 3) one at the balance point for portaging. A minimum is 3 for a 15' boat; 4 for an 18' boat; 5 for anything larger. One extra thwart is recommended for white water. Make them from 1"x3" ash strips, and attach to the gunwale.

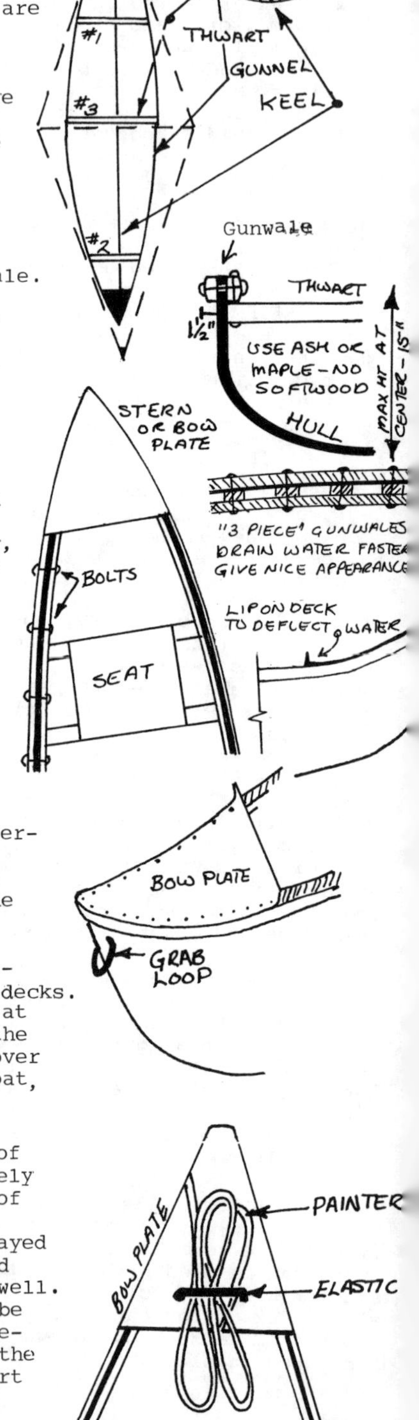

GUNWALES can be made from 1½" x 3/4" ash lathe screwed or bolted into place around the edge of the canoe. Take care not to leave any sharp edges of fasteners protruding. Since the gunwale serve as anchors for the thwarts it is best to start at one end and move to the other, attaching the thwarts as you go. This is what gives the canoe its shape; if your's comes out funny, change the length of the thwarts or move them about until satisfied. Try not to bend the hull out of shape when you are done.

SEATS can be made by placing two thwarts 9"-12" apart and covering them with fiberglass or canvas as shown. These are a great relief to anyone who paddles flat water, as kneeling can be terribly tiring.

THE BOW AND STERN PLATES ADD considerable strength to the ends (another triangle) and can keep out at least some water if properly designed. The National Open Canoe Championship specifications limit the length to 36". Some long-distance cruising desighs will use fuller, even total, decks. The height of the splash deflector at the end of the bow, which directs the water which falls onto the "deck" over the sides, keeping it out of the boat, is limited to 1".

THE BOW AND STERN LINE can consist of either grab loops or painters securely anchored into a reinforced section of the bow. Drilling a hole high up on the bow or stern, inserting the frayed end of a rope, and covering that end with fiberglass cloth works pretty well. If a full painter is used, it must be kep out of the way to avoid entanglement problems. On the deck towards the back drill two holes 5" apart, insert shock cord through these holes, and tie off the ends. The painters can then be coiled and forced under this shock cord, where it will stay until needed.

FLOTATION is an important consideration for the builders of fiberglass boats. Without it, your boat will simply sink to the bottom when swamped. The minimum amount of flotation needed to support the canoe, two people, and gear is about 2.5 cubic feet in each end. Additional side flotation will increase stability when swamped and make it much easier to execute "the capistrano flip" and other deep-water self-rescue techniques. In white water, flotation displaces water, reducing the drag of the current and floating the canoe higher, where it is harder to pin and less susceptible to damage

THE ENDS of a canoe under the deck can be closed off with an Ethafoam bulkhead fiberglassed in place, creating an air chamber. The ends can also be filled with contoured styrofoam blocks. The use of "pour in place" foam for this application is not recommended, as this makes the boat extremely heavy.

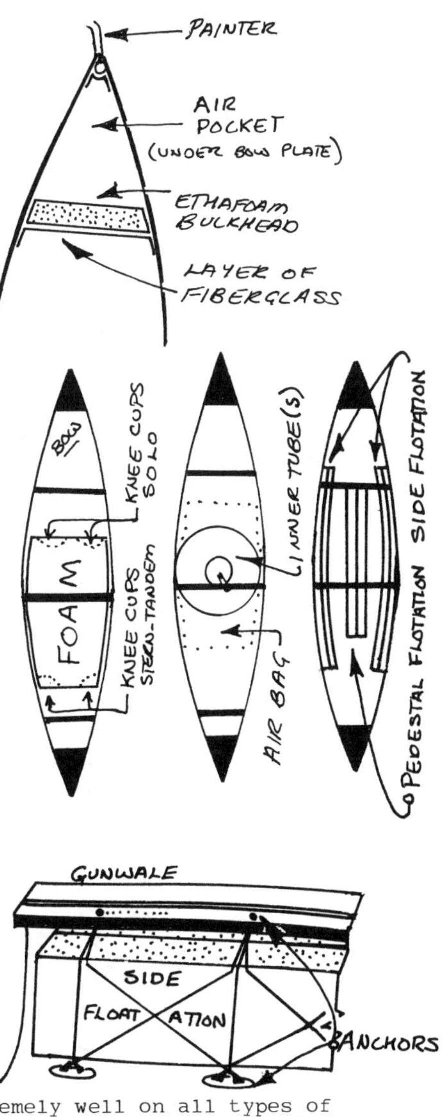

THE CENTER can be filled with inflated truck inner tubes (purchased at low costs from your friendly local truckstop), but these are heavy. Special open canoe air bags (or C-2 center bags) can be purchased through a white water outfitter. The Nantahala Outdoor Center uses huge blocks of styrofoam which completely fill the center of the open canoe. If placed properly, the solo paddler and the stern paddler of a tandem team can cut knee holes into the foam for support. This is a very heavy, but effective rig. Such boats are almost impossible to pin or damage, since the foam provides both buoyancy and support.

The Coastal Canoeists and other whitewater specialists prefer to take 2"x12"x5' planks of Ethafoam and lace them to the side of the boat under the gunwhales. One-ply is great for flat water use; two ply for white water. Knee cups can be cut into this foam fairly easily. Flotation can also be provided with an extra-wide center bulkhead which doubles as a seat. Braced under the thwarts, it gives extra support to the hull in much the same way as an Ethafoam wall.

These flotation additions work extremely well on all types of canoes and are recommended especially for ABS canoes which do not have sufficient flotation even for flat water use.

FITTINGS are a matter of taste. Some purists will not want thigh straps and knee pads, others will want "the works." Anything you add is going to improve your boat control, so don't hold back ! See the section on "outfitting" for C-1's and C-2's.

ONE OUTFITTING TECHNIQUE uses the thwarts to anchor a pedestal seat, which is contoured at the sides and under a thwart immediately ahead to form thigh straps and underneath to make knee cups. The results are super, and the extra flotation is a real plus.

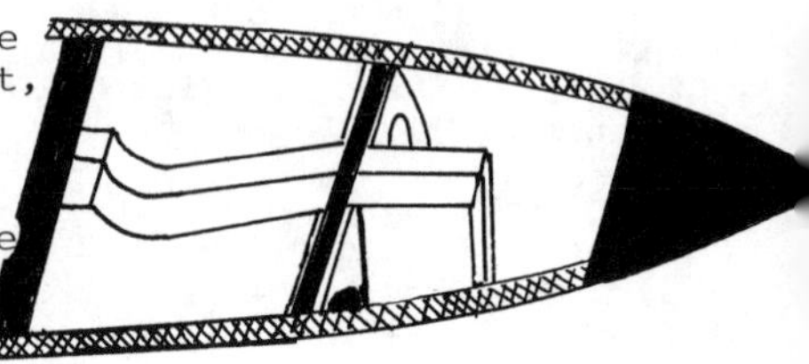

ACA OPEN CANOE RACING SPECIFICATIONS:

With increased interest in open canoe racing many of my readers are designing hot canoes. I am therefore printing the ACA open canoe specifications in their entirity.

A WHITEWATER OPEN CANOE is a traditional open Canadian orIndian design, which is a boat with both ends pointed and higher than the middle, symmetrical side to side, and propelled with a single bladed paddle.

WIDTH shall be at least 14.375 percent of overall length at a point within one foot of the center of the hull when measured at the four inch waterline (including the keel).

LENGTH shall be measured along the centerline of the hull as follows:

SLALOM CLASSES: Minimum length
- OC-1 Short: 4 meters; 13'1½"
- OC-1 Medium: 15 feet
- OC-2 15 feet

DOWNRIVER CLASSES: maximum length
- OC-2 Short: Minimum 15'; Maximum 16'6; Min weight 45 lb.
- OC-2: Up to 18.6'; Minimum weight 55 lbs.
-)C-1: Minimum 4 meters; Maximum 18'6; Minimum wt: 40 lb.

It is not permissable to make the boat meet these dimensions with taped-on extensions. The boat must be designed to, and remain within the required dimensions during the competition.

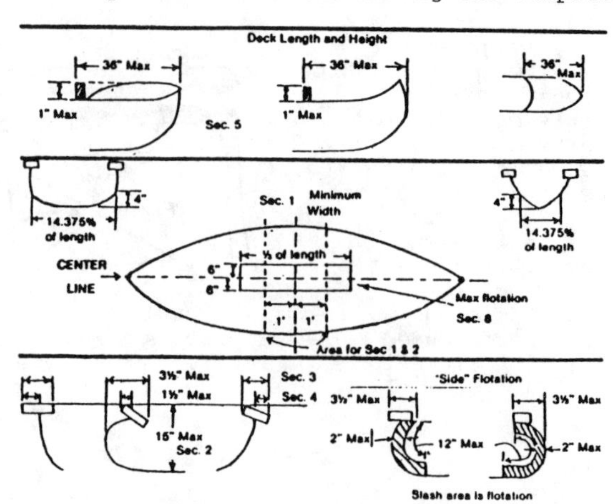

NO BAILING DEVICES other than sponges or scoops.

FLOTATION shall be sufficient to float the canoe if swamped.It shall be limited to the volume under the decks. Additional flotation shall not be higher than the gunwales, shall be no more than six inches from the centerline of the canoe, or shall be under permissable gunwales. You may not use center and side flotation together. Side flotation shall be no more than 2" thick and one foot wide. Canoes outfitted with side flotation are permitted pedestal seats using up to one cubic foot of foam each. Flotation shall not be arranged to impede the flow of water towards the bottom of the canoe.

CANOE COVERS or any other device or material other than normal seats, thwarts, and decks are not permitted. Attachments to the hull other than painters or grab loops are not permitted.

SAFETY LINES of ¼" diameter and 6' length or grab loops ¼" in diameter and 6" long must be attached to each end of the canoe.

GUNWALES may not overhang the sides of the canoe by more than 1½". Total width may not excede 3".

FOR MORE INFORMATION CONTACT: American Canoe Assn., Box 248, Lorton, VA 22079. You must be a member to race in the nationals.

FIBERGLASSING WOOD CANOES (strippers):

Many people have written for guidelines on applying fiberglass to wood canoes, either to put the final touch on a home-made stripper or to restore an old wood-and-canvas craft. We recommend using the WEST epoxy system available from Gaugeon Brothers (address in supplier's list).

1) Remove all hardware, outside gunwale, and keels from wood and canvas boats before stripping the canvas off. Both new and old canoes will have to have all chinks and irregularities in the hull filled with body putty. Chose the putty carefully so it won't show through a clear layup, or use a heavily pigmented resin as a coverup. Sand the entire surface smooth.

2) Drape the canoe with 10 oz fiberglass cloth. The width should be sufficent to cover the entire boat. Cut the cloth to shape in the bow and stern to achieve a good fit. Cut two 4" wide bias cut strips of fiberglass to cover the bow and and stern where the cloth ends.

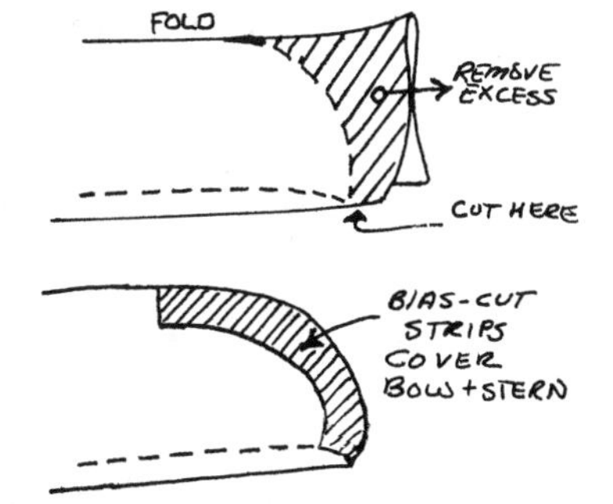

3) Apply a coat of resin to the boat, then lay on the cloth. Saturate in place. Cover the bow and stern with bias-cut fiberglass strips. Allow to cure.

4) After curing, sand the boat smooth with successively fine grits of sandpaper. This will remove the cloth patter and leave a smooth finish. A light coat of resin applied as thin as possible with a block of foam will leave a perfect gloss. Don't use a paintbrush; it will leave bristle patterns and drips behind. VERY LITTLE RESIN is needed for the right effect.

5) Reassemble the gunwales, keels, and fittings.

SOURCES OF SUPPLY:

When I built my first C-1, buying materials was a real adventure. Certain individuals within the paddling community purchased items in bulk; making the connection and picking up all the required items was time consuming and frustrating. Now there are a large number of suppliers of high quality laminating resins and cloths, giving every paddler the access and convenience formerly limited to members of clubs with strong boatbuilding programs. This is just as well, since the increasing use of "tupperware boats," many clubs no longer have materials available.

Any persom wishing to have their mail-order services listed in this book is invited to write the author at Box 447, Penllyn, PA 19422. (****) means I have had good experience with the listing.

ASTRO CHEMICAL COMPANY, P.O. Box 200, Ballston Lake, NY 12019. Phone 518-399-5338. Astro is an epoxy specialist who carries most types of resins and hardeners available in the U.S. Their "System 3387" is an excellent low-viscosity epoxy for hand layup. They are also willing to share information with knowledgeable fabricators over the phone

ADVANCED COMPOSITE FABRICS, 296 Sandy Drive, Boulder, CO 80302. Phone 303-939-9073. This is the source for S-Glass and Kevlar at reasonable prices. A monograph called "Advanced Fabrication Techniques" is available.

COLORADO KAYAK SUPPLY, Box 3059, Buena Vista, CO 81211. Phone: 800-535-3565. CYS sells a complete line of vinylester based boatbuilding materials including pigments, mold releases, and tools. No S-Glass or Kevlar. (****) Accepts credit cards.

DEFENDER INDUSTRIES, 255 Main Street, New Rochelle, NY 10810. (No phone orders). Caters to the marine trade with a wide variety of materials and tools. Much of what they sell is useful to the whitewater craftsperson. Includes Polyester, Epoxy, Fiiberglass, and tools. Catalogue available.

FIBRE GLAST DEVELOPMENTS, 1944 Neva Drive, Dayton, OH 45414. Phone 800-821-3283. These folks are an excellent supplier of high-quality resins, cloths and tools for boatbuilding. They carry pigments, mold releases, books, and other useful items and offer intelligent advice and fast delivery. (****) Accepts credit cards. My personal favorite

GAUGEON BROTHERS, P.O. Box 908, Bay City, MI 49707. Phone 517-684-7286. Gaugeon Brothers are best known for pioneering work in the field of wood/epoxy laminates. Many wood paddle makers usde their materials. They also have lightweight epoxy/carbon fiber system use on airplanes and racing sailboats. Their catalogue contains much useful technical information.

HOOFERS OUTING CLUB, 800 Langdon Street, Madison, WI 53706. Phone: 608-262-1630. This is one of the last of the big-time club building programs (Steve Rock's alma mater). They have an active program of building and instruction; they sell materials (no mail order) and welcome participation from people outside the University. Nice folks.

BILL MCKNIGHT, 7561 Morgan Road, Woodbine, MD 21797. Phone 410-795-7332. McKnight, a former semi-commercial builder, rents molds and does high-quality repair work on fiberglass and ABS. He is the author of *Build Your Own Kayak or Canoe*. Call for availability. His book is nicely put together and easy to follow, with many illustrations.

NEW WAVE KAYAKS, 2535 Roundtop Road, Middleton, PA 17057. Phone 717-944-6320. Owner John Scriner sells COREMAT as well as producing a full line of canoe and kayaks, from squirt boats to touring designs. He also manufactures surfskis. Catalogue available.

NOAH INTERNATIONAL, Route 4, P.O. Box 4638, Blairsville, GA 30512. Phone 706-745-6056. Owner Vladmir Vahana is responsible for the development of CAP polyester cloth. He sells vinlyester resins and fiberglass cloth in addition to this material and has designed a number of interesting kayaks.

PLASTICARE, 1952 W. Union Avenue, Englewood, CO 80110. Phone 800-878-1396. Sells epoxy, polyester resin, fiberglass and kevlar cloth.

PLASTICRAFTS, 2800 Speer Blvd., Denver, CO 80211. Phone 303-744-3700. Sells a wide variety of plastics including polyester resins and fiberglass cloth. Excellent selection of mold releases and tools.

JOHN R. SWEET, US 220 South, Musto, VA 24468. Phone 703-468-2222. Sells epoxy, polyester and vinylester resin, nylon, E-Glass and Kevlar as well as an assortment of protective gear, tools, pigment, and mold releases at very resonable prices. Price sheets available. If you phone, pleas call after 10 a.m. eastern.

WILDWATER DESIGNS, LTD., 230 Penllyn Pike, Penllyn, PA 19422. Phone 215-646-5034. A full-line retailer of whitewater equipmewnt. They stock neoprene, wetsuit glue, shock cord, webbing, thwarts and seats, backbands, and foam. Owner Charlie Walbridge wrote this book. Fast mail order service. Catalogue available. Accepts credit cards.

BULK ORDERS for club building programs are accepted by Advanced Composite Fabrics and John Sweet. When dealing in roll quantities (125+ yards) or drum quantities (5+ gallons), they will give discounts comparable to those found at all but the biggest wholesalers...sometimes more! They are considerably easier to deal with than wholesale sources, since they understand your needs and so not need $10,000 orders to get interested.

<u>MAIL-ORDER EQUIPMENT SOURCES</u>:

CASCADE OUTFITTERS, 145 Pioneer Parkway, Springfield, OR 97477. Phone 800-223-7238. Accepts credit cards.

NANTAHALA OUTDOOR CENTER, 13077 Highway 19, Bryson City, NC 28713-9114. Phone 800-367-3521. Accepts Credit Cards.

NORSE PADDLE COMPANY, P.O. Box 242-C, Spring Mills, PA 16875. Phone 814-422-8844. Fiberglass paddles sales. No Credit Cards.

REI (Recreational Equipment Inc.) P.O. Box 1938, Sumner, WA 98390-0800. Phone 800-828-5533. Catalog Available.

WHOLESALE SOURCES:

Dealing with wholesalers is difficult. They are geared to dealing with industrial users and are wary of individual purchasers. And, since minimum orders are generally 125+ yds cloth; 5 gallons of resin, there's the problem of divvying up the booty afterwards. But if you have a large building program (club or school), the savings can be substantial. Your best source is a local dealer, but if he doesn't have what you want (Boise, Idaho won't have much of a plastics industry) check the Thomas Register of Industrial Manufacturers in your local library under Plastics, reinforced. The yellow pages of major cities are also good sources. Foams may be found under packaging materials also.

1) WRITE on a letterhead or (better yet) CALL during business hours. Most firms are geared to doing business over the phone. Identify yourself as a company (make up a name) or an organization (a canoe club). Most places have a policy of not dealing with individuals.

2) KNOW WHAT YOU WANT. Most wholesalers will not give extensive technical information; a few are ignorant, most just don't like to hassle with small buyers. They will supply data sheets and talk with people who seem to know what they are doing. Read this book carefully and study the data sheets before asking a lot of questions. Occasionally you will find a talkative sales engineer. Cultivate him; they're almost an endangered species !

3) BE READY TO PAY IN FULL with your order. Most companies will not extend credit. Besides, paying in full lowers their costs and makes you a desirable customer rather than a drain on their resources. Be sure to mention that you plan to pay in full when you order; it may entitle you to a discount !

4) ARRANGE DELIVERY, which will probably have to be by truck, since UPS has a limit of 50 lbs. Use a commercial address if you can; most truckers get lost in residential areas, get hassled by having to jockey their rig in tight places, and charge extra because of this. Oftentimes a gas station or local merchant will cooperate. If not, ask that the material be held at a warehouse so you can call for it (or arrange delivery) at your leisure. Many warehouses are open 24 hours a day, so pickup can be easily arranged. Just remember that warehouses are located in the roughest parts of town.

5) Don't quibble about minor variations in quantity, particularly of cloth. Wholesalers deal in "full rolls" and standard quantities; they don't like to adjust these units (often they won't) and charge horrendous prices for doing it. It's cheaper not to quibble.

6) TAKE THE SALESMAN'S NAME. That way, if something goes wrong, you'll have someone to hassle on the other end of the line. Most companies send written confirmation of their orders (ask), so if you don't get an acknowledgement within a week or two, call in and double check. Ask if the stuff is in stock and for an estimate on delivery. Unless you are so pushy that a salesman has to lie to get rid of you, you'll get pretty accurate info this way. Buying through a local distributor minimizes hassle, and is worth the extra $$$'s.

7) TO AVOID DOUBLE-BILLING AND DOUBLE SHIPMENT, if you send in a letter or purchase order, always specify that it is a confirmation of a phone order placed with so-and-so on such and such a date (if, in fact, it is).

MOLDMAKING:

The forgoing assumes that you have a fully-prepared, legal plug available. Please note that this is a job requiring more time and skill than building a boat, and that lapses in craftsmanship can have serious effects on the boats which come out of the mold.

1) THE PLUG MUST BE PERFECTLY SMOOTH. If it is not, polish with successive applications of 200,400, and 600 grit wet sand paper mounted on a hard block.

2) MEASURE THE PLUG FOR LEGALITY. It's very annoying to have to contend with a mold which produces boats which are too narrow or short to pass boat measurements at races (not to mention an incredible hassle for racers and officials who find this out at the last minute)

3) ATTACH A FLANGE TO THE PLUG by one of the following two methods (and as a favor to vacuum-baggers, make the flange at least 3" wide)

THE EASY WAY is to glue strips of 2" thick Ethafoam to the side of the plug Several strips can be butt-joined if necessary with glue to form a continuous flange. This requires no special skill or tools and will not damage the boat. Use contact cement, rather than resin, for easier cleanup.

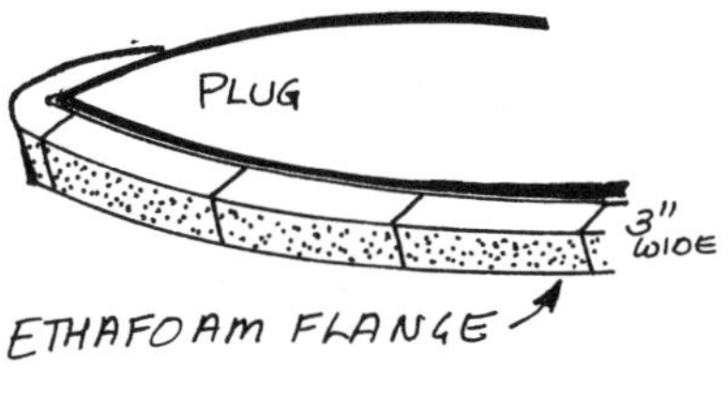

IF THE ABOVE IS NOT POSSIBLE, you can make a flange from ¼" plywood. Have someone hold the plywood sheet next to the boat as shown. They must not move it while you work ! Using a pencil braced against a carpenter's square (or through a hole if you are willing to drill one) slide the square along the side of the plug, tracing an outline of the shape of its side onto the plywood. Cut out and butt against the plug, holding it in place with L-brackets screwed in at the seam line. Tape the underside, and fill in the chinks with modeling clay.

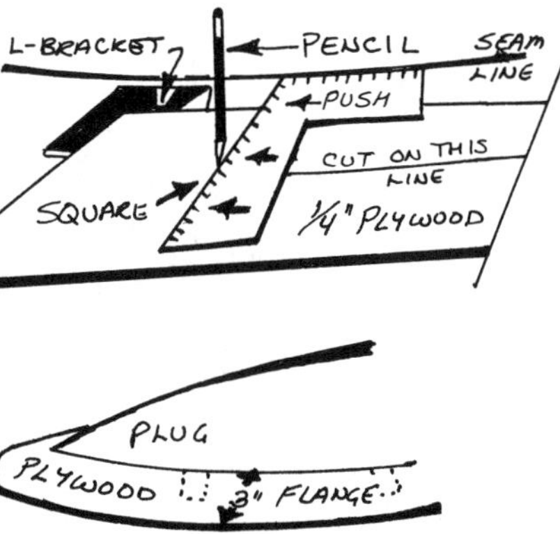

WHEN THE FLANGE IS ATTACHED, use large half-round upholstery tacks driven into the flange to serve as alignment points. When the indentations of one flange nest with the protrusions in its opposite, alignment of the two mold halves is easy.

4) WAX THE ENTIRE PLUG AND FLANGE with 3-6 coats of wax. Apply 1+ layer of PVA to the hull, 2 to the flange.

5) LAY DOWN A GEL COAT over both the half you are going to mold and the flange. Allow to set up, but not to cure completely. It should still be tacky for successive layers to adhere properly.

6) LAY THE HULL OR DECK UP AS FOLLOWS: 1 layer of mat across the hull or deck to the edge of the flange; 1 layer of mat across the flange to the side of the boat; a reinforcing layer along the edge of the deck or hull out to the flange; another layer over the flange to the hull; a single strand of roving in the corner between the flange and the boat; a strip of mat over this corner; two layers of reinforcement around the cockpit rim; a layer of mat over everything; then several layers of mat (2) or woven roving (1).

COCKPIT HOLE
USE 4 OZ MAT
FLANGE
MOLD LAYUP from Byde

The above layup is taken from Byde, Alan: Canoe Building in Glass Reinforced Plastics; Adam and Charles Black; London 1974 Its purpose is to build up a strong edge which will take a lot of punishment and continue to be of value when seaming. The temptation, as he says, is to put a layer across both the boat and flange right away. Air bubbles form, which are removed by resin flooding, and so the corner ends up being made mostly from resin and is quite brittle. Steve Rock feels that merely laying a strand of roving (pulled from woven roving) is not good enough, as an errant trimming blade can easily excise the whole thing from the mold. The above book is an excellent source of mold and plug building information. It was brought to my attention by O.K. Goodwin of Newport News, Va.

7) When the first half of the mold has cured, strip off the flange and do the other side as follows: clean the places where the flange was attached; wax and PVA the plug and the newly formed flange formed by the completed half of the mold; lay up as before.

8) Purchase 16 machine bolts, 16 wing nuts, and 32 washers (the 1¼" length is best, with full-length threads). Drill the flange at the bow and stern, and at regular intervals. Do not install the bolts; save them in a plastic jar.

9) POP THE MOLD by prying the flanges apart, then lifting the plug out (see section on popping boats). Trim flange & rim.

10) ATTACH FORMS to the mold to allow for easy storage and cartopping. I recommend Ethafoam forms. If you must use plywood, the frame should contact the mold at the flanges only. If the frame goes all the way across the bottom of the mold, it will leave an imprint, deforming its original shape. A mold blocked with Ethafoam is easily carried without using a rack. (see below)

11) MARK THE BOW AND STERN INDELIBLY on both halves of the mold. Using the technique described for "straps" in C-1 outfitting, attach bow and stern "grab loops" at both ends for safer cartopping.

12) WAX THE THREADS OF THE BOLTS, and bolt the mold together. Store on edge in a safe place.

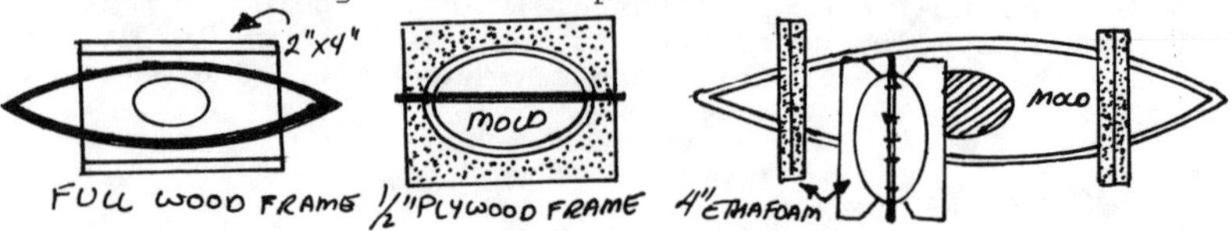

MAKING YOUR OWN PLUG:

NB: Boat designing is emphatically NOT for everyone. Unless you know what you are doing and are willing to experiment, your chances of coming up with a <u>real dog</u> are excellent. It is much safer to rent a legal mold or to make arrangements with the manufacturer (or, immorally, to rip him off). If you wonder why the manufacturers get so uptight, maybe you <u>ought</u> to try the following:

1) Obtain cross-sectional drawings of the desired shape at regular intervals (how you get these is your problem !). These should be slightly undersized (you'll see why in a minute). Cut them out in ½" plywood.

2) Obtain a 2"x2" "spine" as long as the intended boat. Thread the cross sections onto the spine at the required intervals and in the right order. Secure in place.

3) Obtain 4-8 laths (thin strips of wood) and nail into place as shown in the diagram below. Midwesterners, who have less white water and more time to fool around, lay up complete "wood-strip" plugs. This is beyond the reach of the average craftsman, but if you are interested, I recommend David Hazen's book: "Stripper's Guide to Canoe Building", available through the ACA book service.

4) Wrap heavy cardboard around the lath frame and nail or staple in place. Take Ethafoam or polyurethane foam blocks, glue them together, and drill a hole into them so they can be slipped onto the spine at the bow and stern. Shape with a knife or shureform file; tape gap between the "end plug" and the cardboard; it should be 1/8" or less.

5) Drape glass mat over half the mold. Staple in place, then saturate with resin. 1-2 layers will give you the rigidity you need for the next step.

6) Sand roughly, removing any high and rough spots, with coarse sandpaper. Then using body putty and a putty knife, fill in all obvious depressions. Major hollows should be covered with several layers of glass mat. Extend each layer well beyond the boundaries of the depression. Do not overfill.

7) Go over the entire surface with fine sandpaper, removing projections visible to the eye. Do not cut too deep, particularly when using power tools. Fill irregularities or holes with body putty. Remove major high points with a flat file.

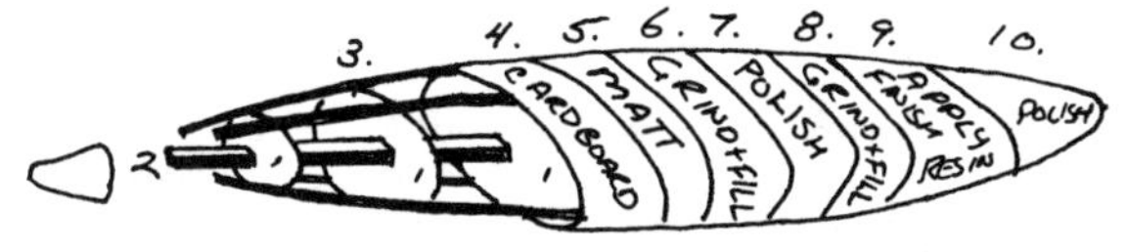

PLUGMAKING – 1 TECHNIQUE (from Byde)

8) Go over the entire mold again with extra-fine sandpaper mounted on a hard block of wood. Cut back ripples and ridges; you eye and hand can pick most of them out. A large crew will speed things up greatly. Continue until bored, then fill in crevices with body putty. Allow to cure, cut back the high places with a file, and sand some more. Continue to the limits of your endurance.

9) Give the entire plug 1-2 light coats of finish resin. Apply with a foam scrap; allow 24 hours to cure. The glossy surface will show waves and wrinkles you never knew existed. Cut and fill where needed.

FINAL POLISHING:

1) Apply 4 coats of finish resin as described above.Allow at least 30 minutes drying time between coats. Allow a 24 hour core. Polish with successive applications of 200, 400, and 600 grit wet sandpaper. Follow with rubbing compound applied with a power buffer. John Scriner of New Wave Kayaks recomends the TR System available from J.M. Thomas at 609-858-5400. He starts with their "Extra Heavy" rubbing compound and follows with their "Sealer Glaze which fills any remaining small pores. This material produces a super-bright, smooth finish on molds, too.

2) Some compulsives recommend making a new plug from the resulting mold, truing it, and making another mold. Seems a bit excessive!

BREAKING IN NEW MOLDS:

For best results, follow this procedure:

1) Allow the mold to cure for at least one week before using it. If you don't wait, you are almost certain to stick your first boat and do considerable mold damage, since the resin adheres exceptionally well to partially cured surfaces.

2) Polish the inside of the mold with 400, 600, and 1200 grit wet sand paper. NB: Anytime you polish a mold, it should be "run in" using the procedure outlined below. Small ridges and irregularities can be cut down at this time.

3) Apply five layers of wax, buffing each one, and allowing six hours drying time between layers so that the wax hardens fully. Apply PVA.

4) Pull the first canoe or kayak. Apply 3 more layers of wax by the above method, then PVA. Take the second canoe.

5) Successive boats can be pulled with only one coat of wax. John Schriner of New Wave Kayaks runs a clean shop; gets 6-8 boats between waxing on well-kept molds.

6) If wax buildup is excessive, obtain a mold-cleaner and apply like wax. It will remove the excess right down to the bare mold. A mold so treated is essentially a new mold, except that three layers, rather than five layers of wax, will be ample protection.

   CAUTION: If the wax and the cleaner are made by the same manufacturer (or even if they are not), don't leave the cleaner lying around the shop. Someone could mistake it for wax, with dire consequences !! (The $300 misunderstanding, in spades !) A cleaned mold looks just like a waxed mold, except it isn't, and even a layer of PVA won't save you from ruining a boat and mold.

MAKING FIBERGLASS PADDLES:

Although a really proficient paddler usually prefers wood paddles to any other, fiberglass is much tougher and longer lasting and is the first choice of most beginners. Both wood and aluminum shafts can be used (the latter is more common), an a metal tip is usually added to retard wear. (Some kayakists omit the tip, but C-1's, who do a lot of poling, should never be without it) Since Aluminum shafts are excessively cold for spring paddling, they must be wrapped in fiberglass or dipped in plastic for comfort.

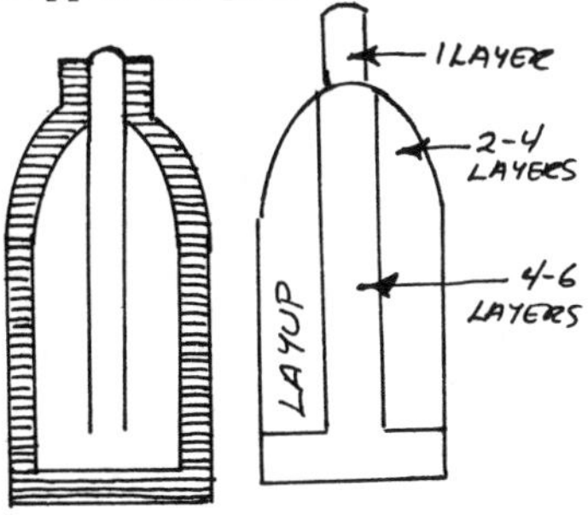

THE BLADE IS NORMALLY LAID UP in a matched "pressure mold" shown at right. You can also lay them up on a "half-mold" by hand with only a slight increase in strength. Epoxy is the resin of choice because of its toughness; fiberglass cloth with a layer of nylon or dynel on the out side to retard wear is also used. (some people prefer an all-glass lay-up for maximum rigidity. Kevlar can be used on the inside. This is most important with wide blades) The most common layup is shown at right. Note that the shaft is inserted into the middle of this layup.

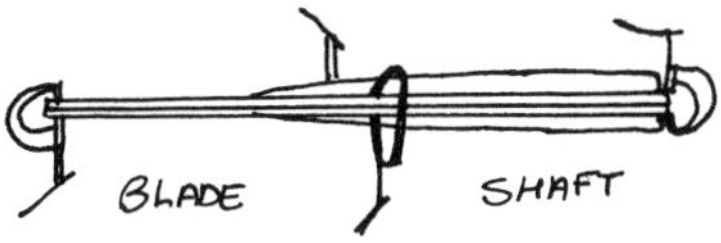

Once the cloth is saturated and in place, bolt the mold together and apply pressure with C-clamps. The more even the pressure, the better the paddle. Hold the mold up to the light (if transparent) and work out air bubbles by varying the pressure on the C-clamps. A hand laid-up paddle is simply left to dry.

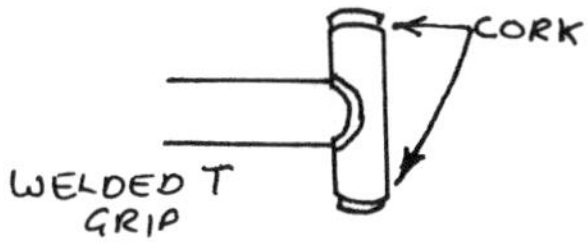

STAINLESS STEEL TIPS (aluminum is a poor second choice) can then be attached to the end with flush rivets. The "sandwich" technique, shown at right, is much easier than the "box-end" technique most commonly used. The tip should not protrude much; if the rivets or any other part stick out, they can catch on a rock without warning and leave you literally "up the creek without a paddle."

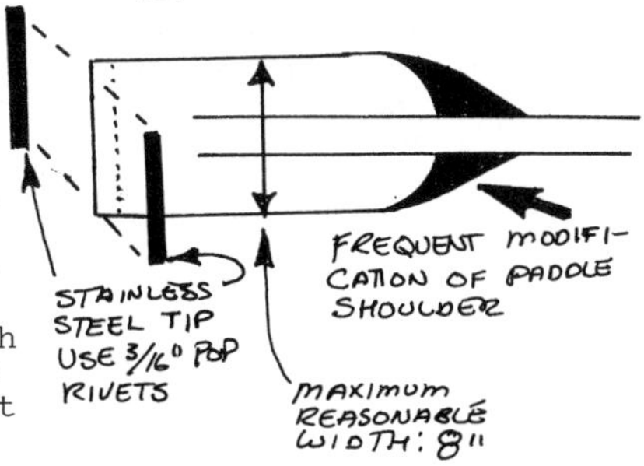

PADDLE MOLDS are hard to find and even harder to make. The best ones extend up the shaft so you can cover it with a layer of fiberglass cloth; if you do not, wrap the shaft with resin-saturated fiberglass tape. T-grips for C-1's can be welded on, carved from wood, or bought from the Norse Paddle Co., P.O. Box 242-C, Spring Mills, PA 16875.

PATCHING:

Sooner or later that inevitable miscalculation leads to the equally inevitable patch. This is the way to fix things up right. Use epoxy or vinylester for patching; it bonds more strongly than polyester. Nylon is an excellent patch material; fiberglass is OK.

"ROUGH AND NASTY" PATCHING:

1) Determine the extent of the damage by scraping away loose bits of resin and cloth with a knife. Cut away delaminated areas (if the area is extensive, use your own judgement !) If the boat has "holed out" completely, back up the hole with tape or (if extensive) wax paper and cardboard so resin will not leak through. Leave the sound part of the hull alone. Jagged edges are O.K.

2) SAND THE AREA around the crack at least 2" wider to each side. Abrade the layup right down to its fibers; you must break thru the gelcoat to get a good bond. If the hole goes deep or all the way through, bevel the edges inward as shown at right.

3) PRECUT CLOTH for patches. 2-3 layers are best for cracks; 4-5 for major breaks. You can cut back a layer or two for racing boats. For best results, patch from both sides; sometimes this isn't possible; don't worry about it. Severe wear points (bow and stern) demand a 7-9 layer patch (except for race boats). When you lay up, overlap the edges to minimize flexibility differences in the patched laminate. The smallest piece goes on the outside; don't ask me why; it just seems to work. The largest patch is next to the break, covering most of the sanded area. Best layup: nylon in, glass out.

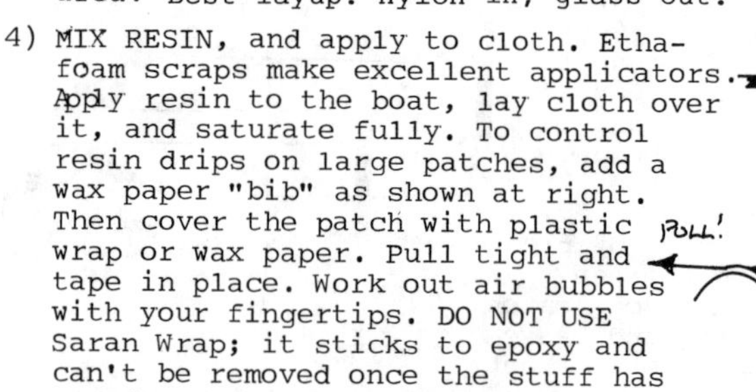

4) MIX RESIN, and apply to cloth. Etha-foam scraps make excellent applicators. Apply resin to the boat, lay cloth over it, and saturate fully. To control resin drips on large patches, add a wax paper "bib" as shown at right. Then cover the patch with plastic wrap or wax paper. Pull tight and tape in place. Work out air bubbles with your fingertips. DO NOT USE Saran Wrap; it sticks to epoxy and can't be removed once the stuff has cured.

This patch is now smooth enough for all practical purposes. A hot racer or repair-cumpulsive type may want to smooth off any ridges or rough edges. I'll let the river do the work. Cheerio !

SMOOTH "PROFESSIONAL" PATCHES:

This technique has been described by Jesse Whittemore and Bill McKnight. It is recommended for people who want something more attractive than the above, and are not adverse to heavy grinding. Remember that power sanders can do considerable violence in the hands of an unskilled user, and be careful!

1) GRIND HULL in an even circle around the break all the way to the last layer. Work slowly; you'll see each layer appear in turn. The last layer will be left paper-thin. Be careful!

2) TWO LAYERS OF NYLON, CAP, OR KEVLAR will form the inner part of the patch. The first piece barely covers the hole; the second overlaps on all sides. Cover with three layers of fiberglass, each one overlapping the other. The final layer should be somewhat larger than the sanded layer.

3) Back up the hole with tape or cardboard. Apply resin, then the cloth, saturating the material completely. Do not cover with plastic. Allow a full cure.

4) Grind the patch flush with the rest of the hull, taking care not to remove too much material. Polish with fine sandpaper to get a good finish. The patch may be polished with 100, 200, and 400 grit paper, then rubbing compound, and coated lightly with resin for a smooth finish. Epoxy paint may be used to match colors if necessary.

GRUNCH PADS:

Grunch pads are useful to racers who must practice on abusive courses in a light boat. The stern is usually the recipient of all the attention, although the bows of wildwater boats can also be helped. Here's how to make one:

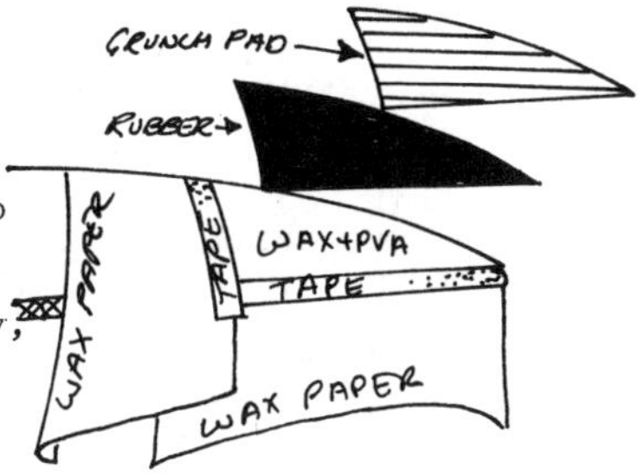

WHEN THE BOAT HAS POPPED, wax, PVA , and mask the last few feet of stern. Lay up a heavy patch, alternating fiberglass and synthetics as you would normally. Allow to cure, then pop and trim. Line the inside with neoprene (inner tube material is OK) and tape securely in place. (VERY securely, or you'll lose it). Remove for racing or less demanding cruising.

RESIN CHEMISTRY:

The forgoing is excerpted from the notes of Jim Colianne, who has done extensive research in this field. It is not intended to be complete, nor is it by any means necessary to build boats. Rather, it is included as a sign of respect for the technological expertise on which our sport depends, and for the interest of those who might be looking for some insight into why things work the way they do. Let's take a look at polyester resins:

POLYESTER RESINS:

All resin systems (and indeed, all synthetic cloths) are polymers, that is, long chain molecules made up of repeating subunits. Polyester resin is formed as a condensation reaction between organic acids (such as maelic acid) and organic alchohols (like ethylene glycol). In a condensation reaction, water is removed, leaving a continuous chain, as follows:

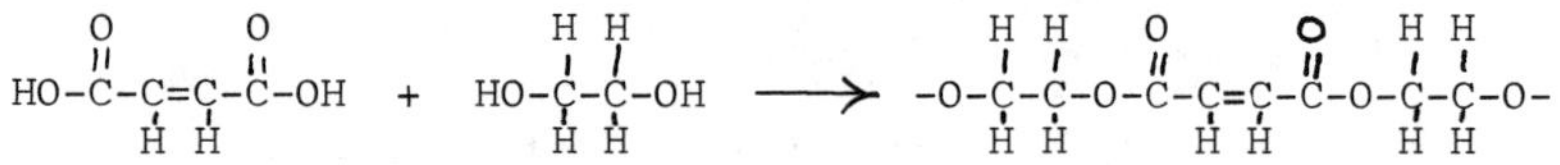

```
     O     O              H H              H H   O     O   H H
     ‖     ‖              | |              | |   ‖     ‖   | |
HO-C-C=C-C-OH   +   HO-C-C-OH   --->   -O-C-C-O-C-C=C-C-O-C-C-O-
       | |              | |              | |     | |       | |
       H H              H H              H H     H H       H H
```

(maelic acid)+(ethylene glycol) = (Polyester Resin)+(Water)

C=Carbon   O=Oxygen   H=Hydrogen   (-)=single bond

The above reaction takes place at the factory. The next step, in which cross-linkages form between the chains, changes the polyester from a liquid to a solid. For this to happen, two thigs are needed: a cross-linking agent (in this case styrene) and a catalyst (such as MEKP). A catalyst does not take part in the reaction, it only helps it get started. MEKP acts by breaking down the double bonds (=) to form single bonds (-) in both the polyester and the styrene, making them susceptable to cross-linkage. As the reaction progresses, the breakdown of the double bonds liberates free radicals (atoms with unpaired electrons), which break down more double bonds. This creates a chain reaction which continues until all the double bonds have been eliminated. As the double bonds dissapear, cross-linkages form, solidifying the material, as follows:

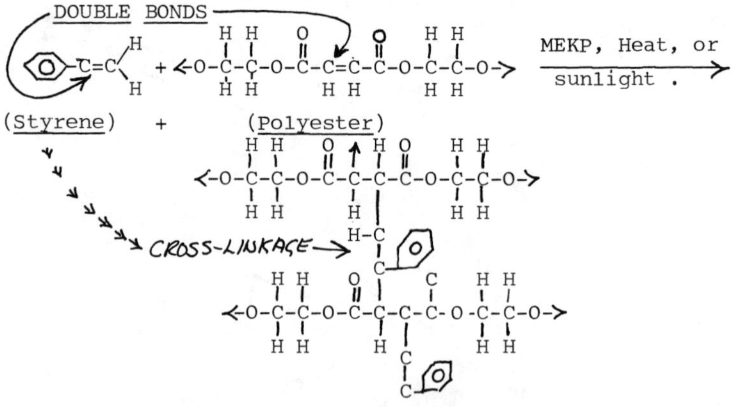

```
 DOUBLE BONDS
                 H H   O     O  H H
        H        | |   ‖     ‖  | |        MEKP, Heat, or
(O)-C=C    + <-O-C-C-O-C-C=C-C-O-C-C-O->   -------------->
        H        | |     | |    | |          sunlight .
                 H H     H H    H H
(Styrene)   +       (Polyester)
                 H H    O  H O   H H
                 | |    ‖  | ‖   | |
             <-O-C-C-O-C-C-C-C-O-C-C-O->
                 | |      |      | |
                 H H      H |    H H
                           H-C
          CROSS-LINKAGE -->  |  (O)
                             C-
              H H    O  |    C   H H
              | |    ‖  |    |   | |
           <-O-C-C-O-C-C-C-C-O-C-C-O->
              | |      |  |      | |
              H H      H  C      H H
                          |  (O)
                          C-
                   Another Chain
```

Flexibility can be controlled by adding other linking agents, in addition to styrene, which vary the length of the cross-linkages. This reaction can be catalyzed by the sun, or will occur spontaneously over time. The reaction is exothermic, that is to say, it liberates heat. Speed is directly proportional to the temperature; the reaction rate doubles for every 18 degree F. rise in temperature. Below 70 degrees F, the reaction slows down substantially. Inhibitors (to prevent premature reaction and lengthen shelf life), promoters (to accelerate reactions) and fillers (such as cab-o-sil) are usually added to most commercial formulations, complicating the above reaction further. Different monomers (components of polyester) may also be used to make up the basic polyester chain. So if you think this is complicated, go crack a chemical engineering text and get really confused !

MAKING NEOPRENE SPRAYSKIRTS:

These are the best sprayskirts money can buy. Everything is glued, so you can make one with no special equipment. You'll need: 2.5' of neoprene, ½ pint of glue, 4.5' of shock cord, three C-clips, and 2' of ¼" nylon rope.

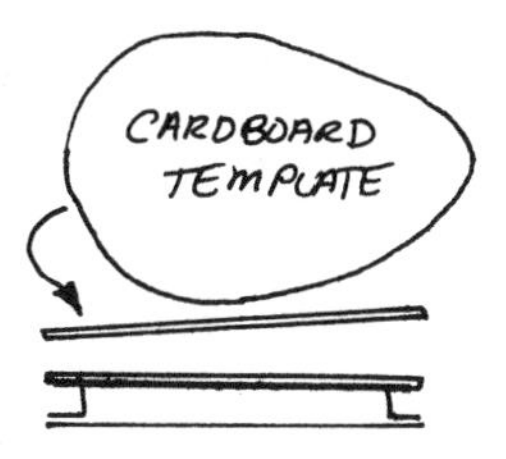

1. Make a cardboard template from a tracing of the cockpit rim. Taped in place, this gives you a smooth working surface for later steps.
2. Scrub the neoprene with a mild soap, or rub with solvent (rubbing alcohol) remove the talcum powder used in packing. This allows the glue to make a strong bond with the rubber.

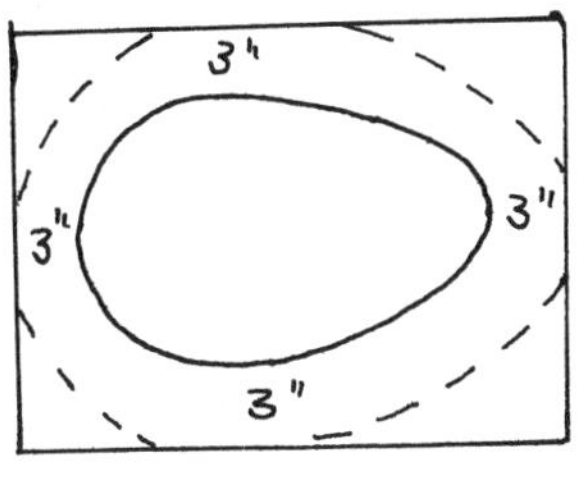

3) Cut out a square of neoprene for the bottom of the sprayskirt, allowing 3" leeway on all sides. To mark neoprene, place it nylon side down, and scratch lightly with a sharp instrument.
4) Slip the shock cord over the neoprene into the coaming and pull tight. It is difficult, but not impossible, to pull too tight. Most people make the opposite mistake, resulting in a sprayskirt which does not stay on in heavy water. If you have a choice, ¼" nylon-coated shock cord is best, as the glue will not stick to the nylon.

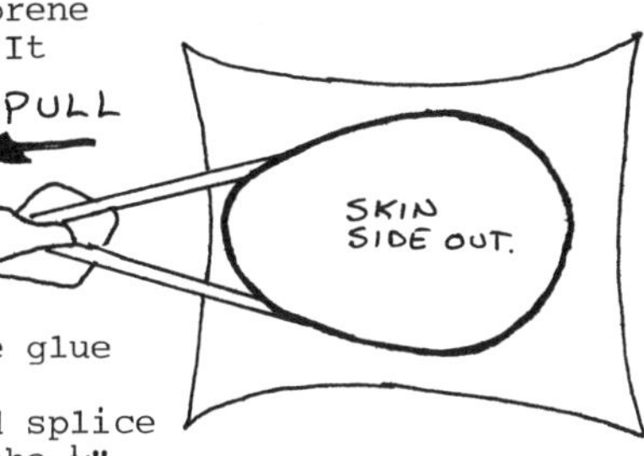

5) Cut the shock cord to length, and splice with C-Clips as shown. Note how the ¼" nylon grab loop is also attached at this time. The clips are compressed together to hold the ends together with pliers. If you can't get stainless steel clips, "Pig Rings" can serve the same purpose. Look for them in a rural hardware store.
6) Slip the cord over the neoprene again. Using the grab loop, check the release. Loosen or tighten as needed. Get into your boat and measure the distances A, B, and C as shown. They will serve as guidelines for cutting the waist hole, as shown. Add 1" to A for kayaks, 3" for C-1's. Cut out the waist band also; a good width is 8"; for length, try 90% of your waist size. Adjust the size of the hole so that its circumference is roughly equal to the length of the waistband.

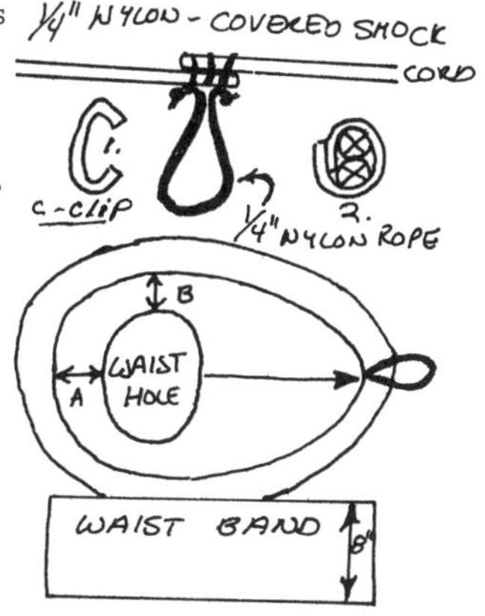

7) Apply wet suit glue to the shaded area on the drawing at right. You'll need three coats. Allow each to dry until tack-free (sticky, but does not pull away when touched) between coats.
8) When the last coat has dried, fold the neoprene margin over in two steps: a) have it stick only to the outside of the cockpit rim and b) fold the rest of the margin over in sections, collecting and trimming the wrinkles, as shown at right. Several big wrinkles are easier to handle than a lot of little ones.
9) Attach the waistband by a) applying three coats of glue to the edges to be joined b) line the edges up and press together c) work your way around the waist hole, attaching the waistband d) when the two ends meet, join them up the back.
10) Complete the job by covering the seam with 3/4"x1/16" neoprene stripping. Note how the edges can be coated with glue and pressed flat.

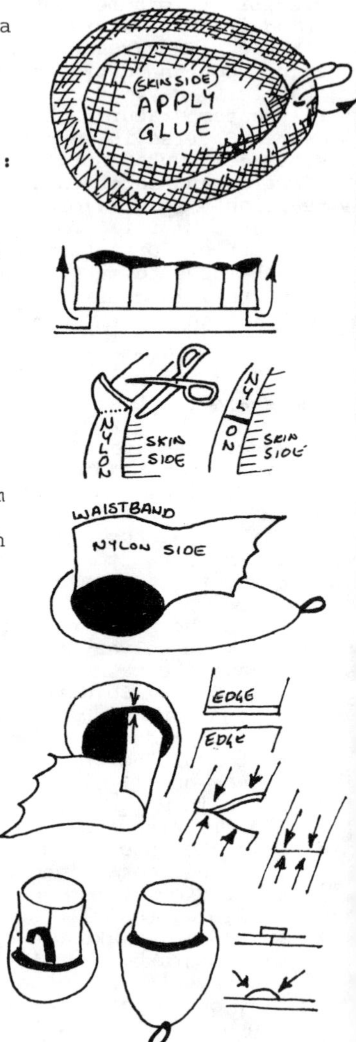

<u>CAUTION</u>: ALWAYS TEST SPRAYSKIRT FOR A SURE RELEASE IN FLAT WATER BEFORE YOU USE IT ON A RIVER.

BEWARE: NEOPRENE GLUE IS FLAMMABLE. VAPORS ARE HARMFUL TO YOUR HEALTH. Use in a well-vented area away from spark or flame.

Complete sprayskirt kits are available from: Wildwater Designs, 230 Penllyn Pike, Penllyn, Pa. 19422. The design is different from the one described above.

HOW TO USE THIS TABLE:

The data at right was developed by Chip Queitzsch as a part of his master's thesis in engineering at the University of Virginia. His tests compare the high-performance fibers (Kevlar and S-Glass) with conventional ones (E-Glass and Nylon). Other materials were not considered due to time limits. Due to the needs of this publication, your editor had to condense this information.

LAYUP: Layers are given inside to outside. Materials are abbreviated as follows: E=E-Glass; S=S-Glass; N=Nylon; P=Polypropylene; K=Kevlar.

WEIGHT: In ounces per square yard. Allows comparisons of strength and weight betweem laminates

CLOTH TO RESIN RATIO: Shows what percentage of a laminate is resin, and what percentage is cloth by weight.

FLEXURAL MODULUS: A direct measurement of stiffness of a laminate.

RELATIVE STIFFNESS: Compare to an all-Kevlar layup.

IMPACT STRENGTH: Resistance to "Sudden loadings"; ie: a good shot from a rock. The higher the better.

INITIATION ENERGY: The energy needed to start a crack in the laminate. The higher the better.

PROPAGATION ENERGY: The resistance of a laminate, once cracked to further damage (ie: propagation of the crack). VERY IMPORTANT TO WHITE WATER PADDLERS, since any flexing may result in hidden damage which can spread.

DUCTILITY INDEX: The lower this figure, the more brittle the layup. Higher figures mean increasing ductility.

From this, we can deduce the following:

1. All fiberglass layups are rigid rather than ductile. They are hard to damage intially (high initiation energy) but once broken, the problem spreads quickly (low propagation energy).

2. All synthetic layups are extremely ductile. They are easily damaged (low initiation energy) but hard to destroy (high propagation energy)

3. Resistance to damage is controlled by the amount of fiberglass in the layup (increases initiation energy). Ability to avoid further destruction is controlled by the amount of synthetic in the layup (increases propagation energy.

4. The addition of all synthetics to a layup except Kevlar increases flexibility. Kevlar does not decrease the rigidity of a layup except in the least desirable combinations. Its value is that it increases propagation energy (resistance to continued destruction) without lowering rigidity.

5. The use of high-technology materials substantially improves the strength of a boat. This is primarily due to the effect of Kevlar; the advantages of S-Glass are less pronounced.

6. Replacing layers of fiberglass with synthetics reduces the weight of each layer by about 30%. The percentage of fiber in the layup by weight is also increased.

EVALUATION TABLE FOR POPULAR LAMINATES:
Data Supplied by Chip Queitzsch

LAYUP	WEIGHT/ Sq. Yd.	COST/ Sq. Yd.	RESIN/ CLOTH RATIO	FLEXURAL MODULUS psi x 10^6	RELATIVE STIFFNESS	IMPACT STRENGTH in-lb./in	DUCTILITY INDEX	INITIATION ENERGY in-lb./in	PROPAGATION ENERGY in-lb/in
EEEE	76.9	16.46	48:52	2.18	1.8	14.0	0.5	9.5	4.5
EENE	72.3	16.19	53:47	1.86	1.6	11.3	4.3	2.2	9.2
ENNE	65.4	15.59	57:43	1.89	1.6	8.6	3.4	2.0	6.7
NEEN	65.9	15.68	57:43	.59	.5	5.7	6.1	.8	4.9
ENEN	65.3	15.55	57:43	1.30	1.1	9.5	4.9	1.6	7.9
KKKK	53.9	32.64	63:37	1.18	1.0	14.5	22.1	.6	13.9
SSSS	62.6	21.39	57:43	2.07	1.7	16.8	.7	10.1	5.7
SKKK	56.4	29.88	62;38	2.13	1.8	17.1	5.0	2.9	14.2
SSKK	58.1	26.98	60:40	2.12	1.8	19.5	2.5	5.5	14.0
SKKS	60.2	27.78	61:39	1.74	1.5	16.3	1.4	6.7	9.6
SPKK	55.9	23.28	62:38	1.79	1.5	14.6	5.9	2.1	12.5

GRAPHS depicting the results of these findings can be found on P. 113. Information on polyester fabric (Diolen) can be found on Page 112. (NOAH Company CAP)

Resin system used was Dow Chemical's VTBN-modified vinylester Derkane XD-8084.03
Reinforcements: 10 oz. E-Glass by Burlington Industries, Chrome Volan Treatment; 4.0 oz. Nylon Style 26115 from Burlington Industries; S-Glass: 5.0 oz style 22022 bought from Clark and Associates(special weaving) and 5.0 oz. Style 181 Kevlar from Clark-Schwebel Polypropylene: 4.6 oz material from Vectra.

Resin was promoted with .4 phr cobalt napthenate and .08 phr dimethylanine then catalyzed with 1 weight per cent MEKP

... thank Mr. Queitzsch for his efforts spent in educating this liberal-arts

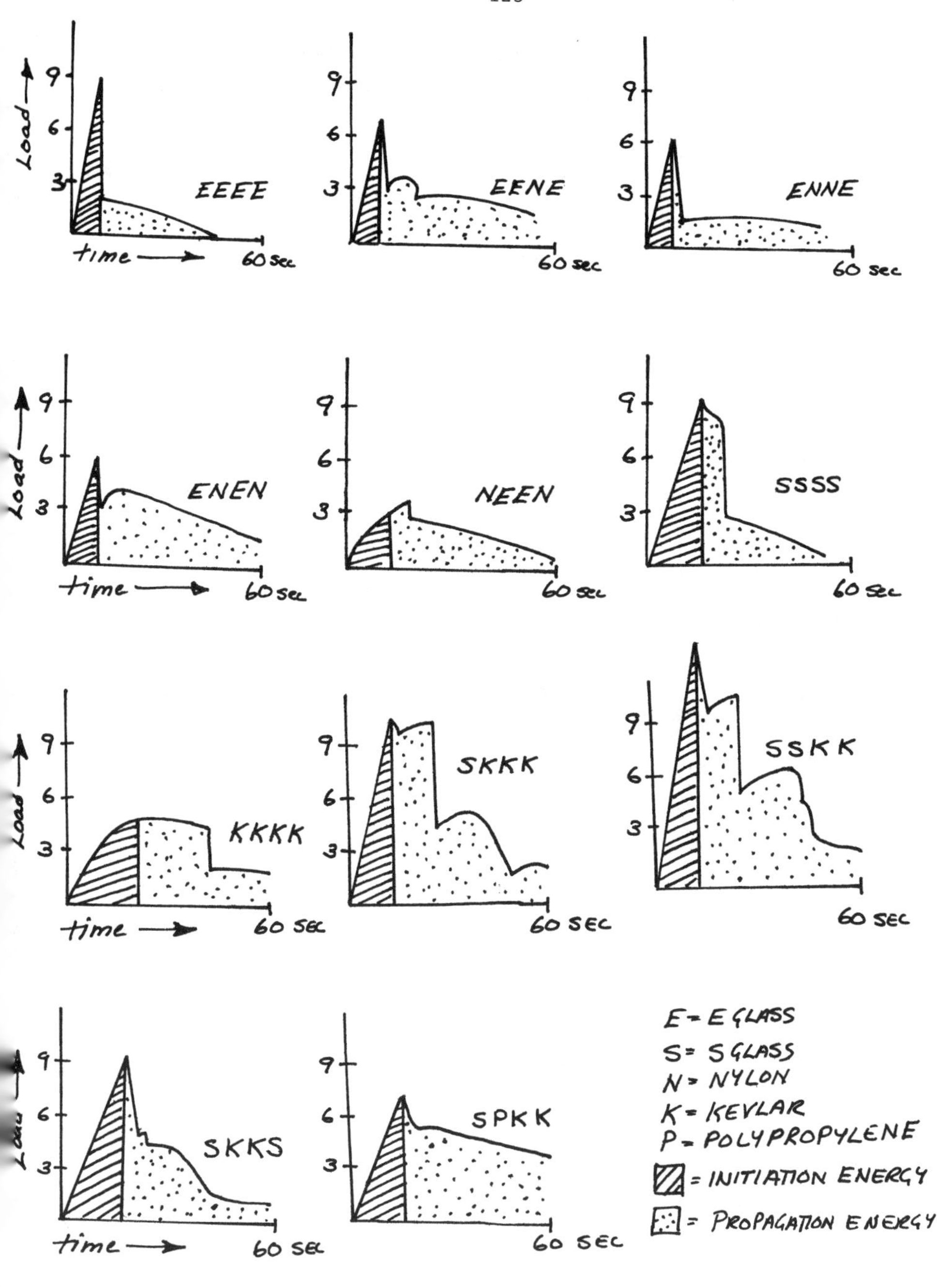

PERFORMANCE GRAPHS FOR POPULAR LAMINATES
by Chip Queitzsch - from Master's Thesis
load normalized to 10 = 50 Kg/in.

TEST RESULTS OF POLYESTER FABRIC COMPOSITES:

This material is similar to Diolen used in European layups, and is sold exclusively in this country through Noah Boats Company of Topton, NC. The information here was supplied by Noah Boats.

Table I

Sample	Flexural Strength		Impact Strength	Graph Label
	PSI	Modulus $x10^6$ psi	rank after testing	
GGGG	29400	1.3	3	A
GGGK	38800	1.7	1	B
GGGP	34300	1.2	2	C

Graph I

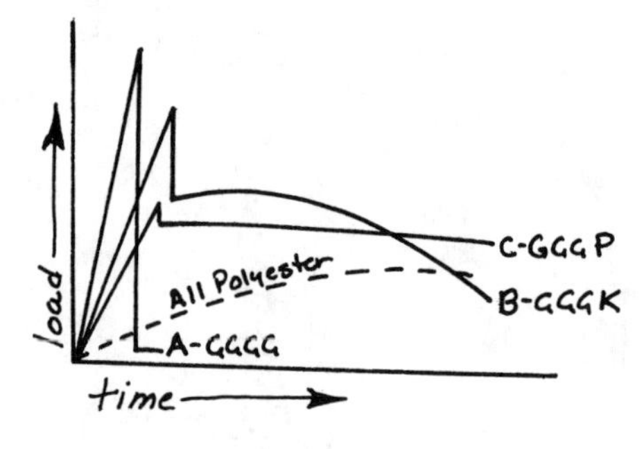

G= FIBERGLASS - 10oz
P= POLYESTER - 7oz
K= KEVLAR - 6oz

CLOTH	WEIGHT oz/sq yd	CLASS	STIFFNESS Scale of 5	STRENGTH: tension / compression	ABRASION RESISTANCE:	RESIN ** ABSORPTION:	COST PER YD. / FABRIC WIDTH
E-Glass	10.0	Fiberglass	4	4/4	4; Smooth	Moderate	3.60/44"
S-Glass	9.0	Fiberglass	5	5/5	5; Smooth	High	6.75/38"
Carbon Fiber	N.A.		5+	2/5+	5; Smooth	High	N.A.
Nylon	4.2	Synthetic	2	2/2	3; Fuzzes	Low	2.90/66"
Polypropylene	4.6	Synthetic	2	2/2	3; Fuzzes	High	4.25/50"
Dynel	4.0	Synthetic	3	2/1	5+; Smooth	V. High	4.00/50"
CAP Polyester	7.0	Synthetic	4	4/4	3; Smooth	Moderate	2.85/50"
Kevlar 49	5.0	Aramid	5	5/3	3; Fuzzes	Low	13.25/50"

All fiberglass-class materials tend to be stiff and brittle.

All synthetic class materials tend to be ductile, thus more flexible and tougher. All have compatability problems with low adhesion resins; their use with polyester is not recommended. Two layers of synthetic should not follow each other.

All Aramids are similar to synthetics, yet stiffer. The same cautions about compatibility apply. Layers can be placed against each other.

NOTE: Most of the above materials were developed for the tire industry (Nylon, Polyester, and now Aramid-belted tires). If you hear about any new fabric used for this application, you may want to see what sort of a boat it'll make.

The author is interested in hearing about experiments with any new material, whether it worked or not.

Table by C. Walbridge

**Resin absorption depends mostly on the weave of the cloth. These figures are for commonly available configurations.